THE ART OF BELONGING

THE ART OF BELONGING

A Memoir

Robert Wolfgang Cahn

Book Guild Publishing
Sussex, England

First published in Great Britain in 2005 by
The Book Guild Ltd
25 High Street
Lewes, Sussex
BN7 2LU

Typesetting in Palatino by
Keyboard Services, Luton, Bedfordshire

Printed in Great Britain by
CPI Bath

A catalogue record for this book is available from
The British Library

ISBN 1 85776 993 7

For Pat, as always

Contents

Foreword

by Professor Freeman Dyson

In wartime London, toward the end of World War Two, austerity had become a way of life and memories of peace were fading. My friend Robert Cahn brought me to his father's flat. The flat was full of the sound of music, a string quartet playing Haydn with passionate intensity. Robert's father was the viola, delicately leading the ensemble and guiding the tempo as he played. While I listened to the music, my eyes strayed over the drawings and etchings on the walls. The flat was full of art as well as music. Robert's father was a collector, specializing in German high baroque. After the music stopped, he showed me his treasures.

That encounter with the Cahn family was for me a revelation. I was a native Englishman, accustomed to living a grubby life under grubby wartime conditions. And here were the Cahns, newly arrived as refugees from Hitler, rebuilding their lives in England with style and elegance. They were teaching us how to defy Hitler, by living as if Hitler had never existed. They were maintaining the aristocratic standards that we had abandoned. After only a few years in England, they belonged to England more than we did. They had mastered the art of belonging.

Robert showed his talent for belonging in other ways too. Mountaineering is the sport in which the sense of belonging is most intense. When you undertake a serious technical climb, you climb on a rope with one or two companions, and you trust your life to your companions' skill. The team on the rope is bonded spiritually as well as physically. To be a serious mountaineer is to belong to a tightly bonded community. So Robert became a mountaineer and his wife did too. Belonging together on the mountains was a good foundation for an enduring marriage.

In his professional life as a scientist, Robert chose an unusual role. He was an editor of technical publications, and his editing work was on a massive scale. He edited four research journals, three technical encyclopedias, and three series of books. For every one of these enterprises, he was the founder as well as the editor. Each time, when he saw the need for a new journal or a new encyclopedia, he persuaded a publisher to publish it, and he set up the organization to produce it. This involved a prodigious amount of work and an ability to collaborate with a prodigious number of people. Every one of the enterprises that he founded was successful, and most of them are still flourishing today. In his rôle as editor, he was a central figure in the community of materials scientists. He had a big share in creating the community. As he says in this book, 'Scientific editing is not an arid, mechanical occupation, but is central to the concerns of what I call the commonwealth of science'. Scientific editing was his way of belonging to the community.

Robert started his professional life as a metallurgist, a specialist in the study of metals. As he broadened his interests to study other kinds of materials, the community of metallurgists broadened its interests too, and metamorphosed into the community of materials scientists. Robert's journals helped the community to evolve. The new discipline of materials science gave intellectual coherence to a wide range of ideas and methods. Materials science emerged as a discipline with its own ways of looking at the works of nature and of human invention. Robert's latest book before this one, *The Coming of Materials Science*, is a history of the discipline that he helped to create.

In recent years there has been big dispute among scientists and philosophers about the relative merits of two kinds of science. Reductionist science aims to explain complicated phenomena by reducing them to their simpler components. Emergent science aims to explain complicated phenomena by finding rules of self-organization that do not depend on detailed knowledge of their component parts. Robert Laughlin, a theoretical physicist, proclaimed the credo of emergent science in a recent article in the *Chronicle of Higher Education*: 'The organization can acquire meaning and life of its own and begin to transcend the parts from which it is made. I have a meaning transcending the atoms from which I am made'. All science is partly reductionist and partly emergent, but the emphasis varies from discipline to discipline. Traditional physics is mainly reductionist. Materials science is mainly emergent. The sociologies of the two disciplines are also different. Traditional physics tends to isolate people in narrow specialities. Materials science tends to bring people together in broader groups. Materials science gives to its practitioners a stronger sense of belonging. That is perhaps another reason why Robert Cahn devoted his life to it.

Freeman Dyson
Princeton, 2005

1

The World Turned Upside Down

My father appeared, unheralded, in his handsome open tourer, and informed the headmaster of my boarding school in the Black Forest that he was taking me off to Switzerland for a short holiday. It was early September 1933; we crossed the Swiss frontier with minimal luggage and a synthetic carefree air, and it was to be nineteen years before I set foot in Germany again.

Papa, mama's father, mama and her lover Karl, together with my younger sister, Irene, and myself, assembled in a luxury hotel in Zürich for a family council. It was an uneasy occasion. Papa and mama had been married for ten years but their marriage had failed: his attention had been fixed elsewhere and she, in despair, had become enamoured of the Gentile artist who had been teaching her the elements of sculpture. My widowed grandfather, Hugo Heinemann, a successful business man, had made our precipitate flight possible. Unlike most German Jews, he had perceived, the year before the Nazis took power, what was afoot in his unhappy country and had deposited a substantial portion of his fortune in an anonymous account in Luxembourg where it was managed by a trusted cousin. His substantial business in its art-nouveau building, with its stock, and our large new villa in its extensive garden in a suburb of the little town of Fürth in Bavaria, with its contents, remained behind to become the booty of the Nazis, who had been in power in Germany since January of that year. Our flight across the border had been apparently light-hearted; but, in fact, my grandfather had to pay a truly exorbitant sum as 'Reichsfluchtsteuer', a tax on flight from the Reich. Soon thereafter, such a flight would have become even more difficult; the Nazis became determined to steal all Jewish property and to reserve Jewish people for eventual transfer to concentration camps. In mid–1933, however, the Nazis were still developing their Jew-baiting skills.

Not long ago, in 2002, I arranged for my grandfather Hugo's gravestone in Fürth to be renovated and for an additional word to be engraved upon it – *Lebensretter*, saver of life. My nephew Tom, who venerates the memory of the great grandfather he had never known and has named his own son for him, contributed to the cost. The saving of life – that was my grandfather's literal gift to all his immediate family, including my errant father.

The family resolved that papa should travel to London, with a modest share of the family money, and there start a new life and do his best to create a business. To leave his hands free, he was not to be burdened initially with the care of either of his children, who were to travel on to Spain together with mama, Hugo and Karl. Why Spain? Karl, the aspirant artist, had visited the country before and judged that there he would be able to earn his crust more easily than elsewhere (he had not been a conspicuous artistic success in Germany); moreover, he knew a little Spanish. Also, the family had heard of an exceptional boarding school on the edge of Palma de Mallorca, in the Balearic Islands, headed by a reportedly virtuoso American teacher; they reckoned that if Irene and I were to be educated there, we would soon learn enough English to be ready to join papa in England, once he had established himself. Papa travelled off to London (I never discovered what became of his splendid car), while the rest of us spent a few days in the small Swiss resort of Engelberg, where my ninth birthday was celebrated. Irene's fifth birthday had been a few weeks earlier. Fifteen years later, I took my new wife to Engelberg on vacation in memory of that early birthday celebration, and we climbed a nearby mountain.

The family travelled to Barcelona by rail. From Barcelona we took the overnight ferry to Palma, the capital of Mallorca, the largest of the Balearic islands. At that time it was a quiet little town, by no means the tourist trap it has since become. Among the tiny handful of foreigners on the island was Robert Graves, the eccentric English poet and scholar. The family found a modest apartment to rent in a Palma suburb, Terreno, while my grandfather settled in a hotel on the waterfront, with his copy of Goethe's *Faust* from which he was inseparable. Irene and I were promptly delivered to the nearby Ecole Internationale, and introduced to Ray Ogden, the headmaster, an American aged around forty. We were bidden to address him as Pitar Ray: 'pitar' is, we learned, Armenian for 'father', and he had adopted this name because this travel-happy man had previously established a transient American school in Armenia, before settling in Mallorca. Pitar Ray transformed my life.

Twenty-one years later, when I was on an academic sabbatical in the USA with my own family, I went to great trouble to locate Pitar Ray – by that time back in his native country and still teaching, at a military academy in Miami as it turned out – and persuaded him to visit me briefly in Baltimore, where I was living that year. He created an instant rapport with our little sons, as he had done with Irene and me in 1933. I apologised to him for having been naughty and troublesome as a small boy. He smiled and said that I had not really been naughty, only unhappy, and that he was overjoyed to meet me again and see that I was happily married to a beautiful wife and with well-adjusted sons in tow. That occasion was highly emotional for me.

Indeed, I was unhappy and disoriented when I arrived in Mallorca. My chaotic family life – of which more anon – was one reason, but not the only one. To be deposited in a school where the dominant language was completely unknown to me, on an island endowed with another unknown language, Spanish – together with the local version of Catalan, Mallorquín – and surrounded by totally strange people, was initially

3

traumatic. My very first lesson proved to be in French, yet another mystifying language. I recall being instructed to read aloud from a textbook, and pronouncing the French word 'haut' as though it were the German word meaning 'skin'; peals of childish laughter greeted my effort. I could just about read print, although I found that the normal typeface in the books I was shown at the school was very different from the Gothic typeface customary in Germany at that time (that was only replaced in Germany by a Roman typeface in 1941). However, the handwriting in use at the school, normal English/American style, was initially beyond me; I knew only the German gothic script, which every schoolchild in Germany learnt at that time. (This, at least, was a problem which did not face Irene, who went to school for the first time with Pitar Ray).

Finally – and this was something which loomed large in my mind – I had lost the company of my favourite great aunt, Philippine Ansbacher (my 'Philitante') who had remained behind in Fürth. Philitante was my grandfather Hugo's elder sister, born in 1856. As I discovered only recently, she had had a terrible life: her husband decamped after a few years' marriage and was never heard from again; her daughter died at the age of six, and her unmarried son when he reached forty-four, leaving her entirely solitary. She lived a few steps from our flat in Fürth and I often went to chat with her, and be fed rolls liberally covered with fat and chives, which led to a lifelong fondness for that herb. When in 1930 my family moved to the new villa in the suburbs, I came back into town at intervals for Hebrew lessons, in a religious school just opposite Philitante's little house, and so I continued to find solace in her company. Not long after I had started at Pitar Ray's school, a parcel arrived for me: it contained a German children's book of the 'X Years Before the Mast' type, by the retired captain of a sailing ship. I seized on this, climbed a tree in the school garden, and settled to read my Philitante's gift at leisure, far from the perplexing children in the schoolyard. This was so comforting that I recall the experience vividly to

4

this day. Sadly, Philitante died not long after, in her late seventies; at least she was spared the extreme cruelty of the local Nazis which had not yet reached its full fury. In due course they murdered many hundreds of the Jews of Fürth.

As I have already said, I established an instant rapport with Pitar Ray, and he had an enormous effect on me during the next two years. Pitar Ray's central educational principle was very simple: as much of the pupils' time as was feasible was dedicated to hearing and discussing Homer's *Iliad* and *Odyssey*. Irene and I learnt English at quite extraordinary speed, French and Spanish less rapidly, and I suppose – though I have forgotten – that there must also have been a little arithmetic, geography and history. I devoured books from the small school library: the first one I can remember was Sir Walter Scott's *Ivanhoe*, which made a deep impression on my Jewish mind – I was especially taken with the beautiful Rebecca. It was followed by the usual boys' adventure stories, by authors like Henty, and I have an idea that Stevenson's marvellous *Treasure Island* also came my way at that time. But the core of the Mallorcan experience was Homer, read in English translation to a mixed-age, mixed-sex group, by Pitar Ray himself. The poems were supplemented by the Greek dramatists' rendition of the events of the Iliad, and I remember a performance of one play – it must have been Aeschylus' *Agamemnon* – which culminated in a scene with Clytemnestra, a tall Spanish teenage girl, one of the pupils, scowling with abandon as she brandished a red-stained axe and hurled imprecations at the corpse of her husband concealed behind a curtain. I discovered with astonishment that others had much more difficult lives than I did. I learnt about gods who shared all the unworthy passions and prejudices of humanity but must at all costs be propitiated, about fierce heroes and male bonding, lightning bolts, femmes fatales, the underworld, many-headed dragons and lethal whirlpools, and a desperate but disregarded prophet. To say that Homer offered a completely novel perspective on life would be a severe understatement: such religion as we learned was focused on Jove, not Jehovah.

Every morning before breakfast we would don swimming costumes and run through the vegetable garden down to the sea to swim for a few minutes, and at other times we would clamber among the wild limestone cliffs behind the school, surrounded by the booming breakers of the open Mediterranean. During the summer break, Pitar Ray would take those of us who remained in the locality to an American-style camp. The tents were erected in a small pine grove at the top of a slope which led down to a glorious, deserted sandy beach; not a soul to be seen. Every morning, we would carry earthenware vessels to a nearby Moorish watchtower in which there was a well, and bring back supplies of precious drinking water. In the evenings we would sit around a campfire and listen to Pitar Ray read to us from a Western adventure novel by Zane Grey.

Today, that romantic, isolated campsite and its deserted beach is occupied by the honkytonk township of Palma Nova, where drunken teenagers stagger along its promenade.

One year after my arrival at Pitar Ray's school, I knew enough English – helped by the fact that to get my dinner I was required to ask for it politely in English – to enter a short-story competition in the local English-language newspaper, under a pseudonym. I remember that I called myself Fred New, which says something about how I now perceived my life. Needless to say, I failed to win, but at least I knew the language well enough to make a respectable attempt. How I wish that I had kept a copy of this youthful effort! My Spanish, however, was far less soundly established, and when a few years later I went to a school in England, the Spanish teacher there decided that I must start the language all over again from the beginning. Now I can speak it fluently and this ability has added much interest to my scientific life.

My schoolfellows in Palma were of both sexes, a wide range of ages and of several nationalities, including a number of American children; this was my first exposure to Americans (and to Coca Cola), and ever since I have felt entirely at ease with both. However, I had no talent for, or experience of, making friends, and cannot remember the names, nor the features, of any of my schoolfellows – except for one 'Sam', who played various minor tricks on me. The same problem pursued me in subsequent schools and it was not till I went to university that the path to friendships really opened. I can only suppose that this initial opaqueness to friendship stemmed from a settled suspicion concerning the goodwill of those around me, well justified by what had happened to me in Germany not long before.

Irene and I spent some of the holidays at school, and some in the apartment in Terreno with mother and Karl (who had now blossomed into Carlos), and occasionally we spoke with our wise grandfather who, however, took great care to preserve his privacy in his hotel. One day, mama and Carlos took us to visit a luxury hotel, newly built on the northern tip of the island, Cap Formentor. I imagine she had read about it before leaving Germany, perhaps in the same newspaper article which had mentioned Pitar Ray's school, and I recall her wistful sipping of an unpretentious cup of tea, thinking back no doubt to days not long before when she had lived in easy luxury.

In the summer of 1934, after Pitar Ray's camp was over, we sailed en famille to the neighbouring island of Ibiza. Anyone who encountered that island before the war would utterly fail to recognize it now. It was quiet and empty, the pretty harbour virtually deserted, only a few fishing boats moored to the long quay. I was left to my own devices and spent long hours trespassing on the fishing vessels (once falling into the harbour); when that palled, I spent even more time haunting a small boatyard, watching the process of building a wooden fishing-boat, the shaping, fitting, smoothing, waterproofing and rigging – a most absorbing pastime. Meanwhile, Carlos painted one of the Ibizan beauties in her golden finery – rather different from a modern female clubber.

On another occasion we spent a short family holiday in

7

the Mallorcan village of Valldemosa, where Frederic Chopin and his mistress, Georges Sand, had lived for a while in a former monastery. We heard a local pianist play Chopin valses, études, nocturnes and mazurkas – my first exposure to great music, indeed to great art, at the age of ten. I especially treasure the memory of one of the nocturnes.*

One day in 1934, papa came from England to visit Irene and me at the school. One of my favourite photographs, of the three of us together, records the occasion. He was in good spirits and clearly things in England were going reasonably well for him. I imagine that he expressed concerns to mama about our being taught American rather than English (not that he would have been familiar with the slight differences) and he may have pressed for Irene and me to be sent to a school run by a real Englishman, in preparation for our planned transfer to London. Whether or not that happened, in the early autumn of 1935, the family uprooted itself again and we all moved to a small rented house, at the edge of the village of San Cugat del Vallès, itself a few kilometres from Barcelona, on the Spanish mainland, and I was sent to an English day-school in Barcelona itself. All I remember of my few months there is a kindly English headmaster who taught

---

*This was opus 15/2, which begins as shown in the extract below.

This marvellous composition has been well described as 'wistful'. It reveals many of the special features of Chopin's compositions – haunting melodies varied in very slight but crucial ways in their repeated appearances, and astonishingly original forms of harmony. I came eventually to recognize that Chopin is the one composer whose music is always instantly recognizable and cannot be confused with any other composer's creations.

me Latin and addressed me as Titus. I do believe that I just reached a level enabling me to struggle through *De bello gallico* – very different from the *Iliad* and the *Odyssey*. Grandfather Hugo, still living in a hotel in Barcelona most of the time, kindly slipped me an occasional quarter peseta with which I was able to buy comics. I certainly had no guidance whatever about what to read, and in any case there were virtually no books at home for they had all been left behind in Fürth or taken to London by papa, and my mother judged that there was no money to buy more – Carlos was not earning appreciably. The whole family must have survived on remittances from Luxembourg. My grandfather's arrangements for safeguarding that money were so effective that the Nazis, when they occupied Luxembourg, never identified it as Jewish property.

Our third year in Spain passed smoothly, until near its end, when I experienced my very first tremors of technological concern, and spent a long time working out just how a train is able to be diverted by a set of points without being derailed. Certainly, neither of my schools offered me any opening at all to the sciences.

In the summer of 1936, the family went on holiday to a small isolated hotel on a slope in the Pyrenees, with a chapel alongside (a very Spanish kind of arrangement). It was a pretty, unpretentious sort of place and Irene and I enjoyed the freedom of the countryside. One morning there was a sudden and extreme commotion. A group of rough-looking men came with axes, invaded the chapel, chopped out the main crucifix and various saints' statues and burnt them on a large bonfire outside the hotel, then vanished as suddenly as they had come. Meanwhile, the priest had fled. The local population and hotel guests watched in disbelief. The Spanish Civil War had begun.

Next morning, Irene and I explored the immediate neighbourhood. A small wayside shrine, a couple of hundred yards from the hotel, had also been desecrated, and the crucifix inside torn out and left on the ground. Irene and I lifted it between us and carried it back to the hotel, because we sensed that the locals were intensely disturbed by the destruction and we thought that maybe they would be pleased to see a barely damaged Christian item. Irene and I were greeted by a group of pious Spanish ladies as though we had been touched by sanctity. It was the only time in my life that I have been thought at all saintly. Indeed, my family nickname at this time was *Roberto el Diablo*, Robert the Devil.

Now, three years after fleeing from Hitler, we were forced to flee once more, because it quickly became clear that events in Catalonia were deteriorating by the day. We returned to San Cugat and packed our possessions. By now, even though hardly any books had been acquired, we still had numerous suitcases to lug around. The only way to get out of Spain, it transpired, since the land frontier had been sealed by the French government, was to fly, and the only available flight, by a ferocious irony, was by Lufthansa to Marseille (and on from there to Germany). So we flew over Barcelona harbour, where a German cruiser was anchored; the plane dipped its wing in salute. Fortunately, no attempt was made to keep us on the plane when we reached Marseille – and a little later we all stood on the Cannebière on the waterfront of Marseille, wondering 'what next?' For Irene and me it was another exciting adventure; for mama, Carlos and grandfather, it must have been a nightmare.

We quickly moved on by train to Geneva, and there found a modest hotel. Papa joined us briefly for yet another council of war (that was no metaphor) and it was decided that he was not quite ready yet to take charge of Irene and me. So the rest of us moved on again, to the north of Italy, the German-speaking South Tyrol which had been annexed by Italy from Austria after the First World War. At that time, in 1936, Italy had not yet begun to move against its Jews: the terrible experiences recorded by that prince among Italian writers, Primo Levi, were still several years in the future. Indeed, the Jews of Italy, especially those in Piedmont, had for centuries been treated significantly better than in other

European countries. I imagine it was this recognition, and the use of the German language in the South Tyrol, which decided my family on that latest destination.

First we visited Bressanone (Brixen in German), staying at the majestic old Elefant Hotel, and then moved on to a modest pensione in the Dolomites. I recall making friends with a detachment of youthful Italian Alpine soldiers, and also exchanging discourtesies with a Hitler Youth who happened to be by. Tact was not my foremost quality as an eleven-year-old. At the beginning of October, Carlos (he retained his Spanish moniker for the rest of his life) took me to Zürich and there deposited me on a flight to London. I was just twelve. Poor Irene was left behind; papa had clearly decided he could afford to look after only one of us at that stage.

My mother, grandfather, Irene and Carlos remained in the South Tyrol. Mussolini was anxious to ingratiate himself with Hitler and things rapidly became worse for Jews in Italy. My grandfather – who lived by himself once again, in Merano – was even interned for a time. Consequently, in 1938, the family uprooted itself once more and was allowed to move to Bern, in Switzerland, where Irene received some excellent schooling. Not long after this move, Austria was annexed by Hitler and the malevolence henceforth radiating from that unhappy land increasingly infected Italy; the move to Bern had been just in time. In 1940, the Swiss government, which was terrified of being swamped by Jewish refugees, forced my family to move on again when their residence permit was about to expire. So they travelled through the 'unoccupied' zone of France, at great danger to life, and safely reached Spain, where the civil war had ended. Fortunately, Franco was determined to keep out of the World War, in spite of Hitler's urging. However, this attitude of Franco's was by no means certain, and so my family could not be sure that the Gestapo would not yet catch up with them. They returned to live in the same villa in San Cugat, remaining there until 1948 when they deemed it safe to return to a liberated Germany, where by that time the initial chaos of post-war life had begun to resolve itself. My sister's schooling in Spain was certainly not of the standard she had enjoyed in Bern.

As for me, the plane bumped over the grass at Croydon Airport (no runways then) and yet another new life began.

2

Beginnings

My parents and their ancestors were all German Jews, thoroughly assimilated in the country of their birth. Presumably, many generations back, ancestors had migrated to Germany from further east, but I have no records of those migrants. My father's parents were more pious than my mother's: indeed, Emil Cahn (1861–1943), my father's father, was cantor in his synagogues in Stuttgart and Munich, at different times. Anyone called Cahn, or Cohn, or Cohen, or Kahn, or Kagan, or Kaganovich, etc., is a member of the group that in Hebrew is called the 'kohanim', descendants of a line of ancient hereditary high-priests, a select group whose Jewishness passes through the paternal line, unlike other Jews, where it is conveyed through the maternal route. Just once, grandfather Emil took me along to the synagogue to witness a service in which he took part. He was a tall man with a bushy red beard and a strong melodious voice. My grandmother Selma (née Weil, 1867–1941) had impressively strong features, determined by genes which passed on undisturbed to a number of her descendants, especially my beloved aunt Stefanie and her granddaughter Michèle. Further in the past, Selma descended from a much-admired manufacturer, Veit Weil (1811–1887), and another group of Veit's numerous progeny carried on in manufacturing.

Veit Weil was born into a poor family in a small German country town and received little education. He experimented with farming, schoolteaching, Talmudic study and commerce in rapid succession before he decided to try his hand at the large-scale manufacture of glue from skin and bones, an activity which was most untypical for a Jew at that time. Over a period of many years he made a thorough success of this enterprise (it even won a prize at an international industrial exhibition in 1854), which persisted through several generations and was finally exported by my father's first cousin Max Sondheimer when he also sought refuge in England in the 1930s.

Veit Weil's daughter Jenny, in 1867, wrote a touching essay, beautifully inscribed, as a 56th birthday gift to her father; this has survived and been translated by one of his numerous descendants. Here is an extract:

> The life of some people offers little of interest; one day gives way to the next; the waves of life virtually roll over them. Often they are very good people but their existence is not now worth recording. The greater part of humanity belongs to their category, people who cannot lift themselves up above everyday doldrums.
>
> It is otherwise with those who have worked themselves up through their own willpower, and what they are now they have reached through hard work. Their lives always offer something that refreshes the spirit and warms the heart and is worth the imitation of striving men.

Jenny went on to heap praise on her father's charitableness and kindness as a father.

Emil Cahn himself experimented in the 1890s with a career as a manufacturer of straw hats, which were in high fashion among the bourgeoisie of that time, before transferring to the world of insurance; he spent the rest of his career, until about 1930, as a senior administrator for a large insurance company. He lived in Stuttgart, then for many years in Munich, returning to Stuttgart again in retirement. My father Martin (1896–1963) was the third of Emil and Selma's four children; as a very young man, he became a sergeant in the German army during the

First World War – not that this helped him in the slightest in 1933. Emil was the only member of my immediate family who fell victim to the Nazis; he and Selma refused to leave Germany, even when my father engineered an opportunity for them to do so in 1938; Selma died in 1941 in her home; Emil was deported soon afterwards to Theresienstadt, where he died in 1943, fortunately before the customary onward transport to Auschwitz.

My maternal grandfather was Hugo Heinemann (1861–1949), he who saved our lives by depositing money outside Germany while he still could. Hugo was one of the sons of Gabriel Heinemann, also of Fürth in Bavaria. Gabriel (1816–1887) seems to have been a most adventurous man, a professional optician, a designer and maker of spectacles. For some years of his life, he was official optician to the King of Naples (how this came about is not recorded), before returning, presumably with the spoils of office in his pocket, to his native town, in the late 1850s. His stay in Naples must have been around the time of the opening of the Italian ghettos, which would have smoothed his path to the royal court. His eldest son disappeared from the record – he had been born in Naples in 1854 or 1855 and apparently yearned for that city after the family returned to Germany. But Hugo, born in 1861 in Germany, clearly inherited his father's adventurousness. In 1886, when he was twenty-four, he teamed up with another adventurer and started a company devoted to the production of high-quality glass sheets for windows and, more particularly, for mirrors: Heinemann und Schwarzmann, Spiegel- und Flachglas GmbH, in Fürth. The glass was not actually melted and rolled out in Fürth – that was done in another region of Germany; what H & S did was to polish the glass to a high standard of flatness and smoothness – to turn it into plate glass, in fact – and then convert some of it into mirrors. This process of 'ennobling' (*Veredelung*) of glass was a major industry in Fürth, and there were many companies large and small, a fair proportion of them founded and operated by Jews. Many of these migrated from nearby Nürnberg, because Nürnberg had fierce trade guilds which kept Jews at arm's length (see

15

Wagner's 'Die Meistersinger' for a tale of mediaeval guild intrigues in that city), whereas Fürth was relaxed and tolerant, and a large Jewish community developed there. 1886 was a time of recovering business confidence after some years of depression, and thus a good time to start a new venture. Presumably, Hugo obtained from his father some of the capital accumulated in Naples. The 1880s was in technical terms an intriguing time for the mirror industry: until then, most mirrors had been made by coating glass with a layer of mercury, while thereafter, this process gave way to the deposition of silver from a silver nitrate solution, as is still done today. It had been firmly established, after many years of refusal to face facts, that the mercury process led to a fatal disease in the workers exposed to mercury vapour for long periods. There is, today, a house in the centre of Fürth which had been used for the mercury process; it is still, after more than a century, so contaminated that access is forbidden.

I never met grandfather's partner, Herr Schwarzmann, so I suppose that grandfather bought him out before I appeared on the scene, rather as my father did with his partner in London in the 1950s.

Heinemann & Schwarzmann was partly protected by my grandfather's faithful Gentile secretary, so that after the War, in 1948, when he and my mother returned to Fürth, he was able to recover the business, now operated by the secretary's husband, whose wife had died shortly before my grandfather's return. In 1962, after my mother's death, under circumstances to be related later, the business was closed down at the behest of my sister and myself, and the premises sold. Today, the business would in any case no longer be viable, because the modern float-glass process, invented in England, has replaced mechanical polishing of sheet glass, and float-glass can be made only by a very large, highly capitalised enterprise. Glass-making and processing, using the latest techniques, is still a major industry in Fürth today.

Taking together Veit Weil's manufacturing acumen, my paternal grandfather's efforts with the straw hats (encouraged no doubt by his Weil wife), my maternal grandfather's achievements in the glass industry, and my father's successful business in London, my ancestors showed considerable commercial ability. None of them, however, showed any interest in science, and my two second cousins – sons of Max Sondheimer, the gluemaker – and I were the only members of the close family to take up scientific careers.

Grandfather Hugo was a man of artistic sensibility. In 1904, when his company was prosperous and presumably plenty of capital had been accumulated, he had a house built on the edge of Fürth to a design by the architect Fritz Walter in the 'Jugendstil', the art nouveau style of design, replete with curves and curlicues, to house the growing business. It is still there today, divided among a number of distinct companies. Later, in 1930, he and my father together (though I am sure that my grandfather was the moving spirit) commissioned an eminent architect of the period, Otto Ernst Schweizer, to design a sizeable villa in the modern flat-roofed style, set in a large suburban garden. During the Nazi period it became a private clinic; my mother was treated there during an illness after her return to Germany, and on my mother's death it was sold. My son Martin's searches on the internet recently located the drawings, because that architect was important enough in German architectural history to rate his own permanent archive. Unfortunately, this elegant house no longer stands. A few years ago it was demolished, because land in that neighbourhood had become so very valuable that it made economic sense to replace one large villa with several smaller, tightly packed houses.

Grandfather Hugo also had another artistic passion: he venerated Goethe, and especially Goethe's masterwork, *Faust*. In exile in Spain, he always had a copy of *Faust* with him, and read in it every day. I have often reflected on Hugo's profound passion for this poetic drama. I believe that his own yearning for experience and for worldly success led him to identify with Goethe's intense character. Hugo was clearly a man who insisted on the best of everything: he owned a golden pocket-watch made by Glashütte, the most renowned company of precision watchmakers of its time. Every evening without fail, even when he was laid low by serious illness, he wound it; so long as his watch was keeping accurate time, he felt sure that his life was protected.

Hugo married in 1896. His pretty bride was Rosa Geiershöfer (1873–1924). Hugo's father had died in 1887, and his mother, Clara, in 1893, so by 1896 he had presumably inherited enough family money to feel quite confident about being able to support a wife and family; Hugo was always a careful man. My mother Else (1896–1962) was the elder of his two daughters; the younger, Lilly, died in 1917, at the age of eighteen, in the nearby town of Erlangen, of an acute inflammation of the sinuses – the family was devastated. Else overheard gossip among the domestic servants which convinced her that her parents thought that 'the wrong daughter had died'. Hugo was a masterful father – as surviving letters between him and Else demonstrate – and he was implacably opposed to the education of women. Else was an extremely intelligent woman who should certainly have gone to university, as my wife's equally intelligent mother had done. But as it was, Else's capacious mind was left unoccupied and she went through life accumulating a vast array of generally unanalysed facts. A refrain of my childhood was her saying: 'Wir wollen uns nur mal erkundigen' ('We'll just make some enquiries'). Hugo did great things for his descendants, but his treatment of Else is hard to come to terms with in retrospect; it blighted her life. Years later, when in 1947 I introduced my newly wedded wife to him in his old age, my grandfather was utterly at a loss to understand why she had wanted to attend university and study English literature.

My grandmother Rosa died in 1924, at the age of fifty-one, a few weeks after my birth; my other grandparents all died in their eighties. I have never been able to discover what the cause of her death was. Her death certificate recorded that she died in a spa some way from Fürth, but her illness is not specified. Much later, in 1962, when my father, Irene and I came to Fürth for the funeral of my mother, we spent an evening with old Fürth friends of his whom he had not seen in thirty years. Rosa's name came up, and I innocently asked what she had died of: my father and his friends looked at each other with a very 'significant' expression and the subject was brusquely changed. Next year my father also died: no-one now survives with any knowledge of the matter. I fear that Rosa may have lost her reason because of the death of her younger daughter and perhaps took her own life, something which the family might well have regarded as deeply disgraceful. Perhaps she hoped for a granddaughter to 'replace' Lilly, and my arrival in 1924, a mere grandson, may have tipped her over the edge. If this speculation is right, she would have had to wait only for another four years for the longed-for replacement, which I think is how my grandfather perceived my little sister Irene when she at length arrived in 1928. Certainly, she was given the middle name 'Lilly'. I can imagine that my masterful grandfather was less than skilful in consoling his grieving wife.

It was perhaps as well that Rosa died before the War; three of her siblings perished during the War in German concentration camps, and the wife of the fourth likewise. I am still in regular contact with Rosa's niece Charlotte Thyes, known as Lotti (born 1911), who survived in wartime Luxembourg, with her Christian husband Auguste, by hiding her Jewish origins. In 1935, during her honeymoon, she visited her uncle, my grandfather Hugo, in Barcelona. She was fond of him and there is a touching photograph of her looking blissful and him looking very dignified.

Large numbers of the Jews of Fürth died at the hands of the Nazis before and during the War. There is a huge memorial to them in the Jewish cemetery in Fürth. When I stood in front of it, I was acutely conscious of how my grandfather, buried just a few steps away, had saved my life and the lives of my parents and sister.

* * *

My parents, Martin and Else, were married in Fürth on 26 June 1923; he was twenty-seven, she twenty-six. They had met the previous winter, I believe while skiing in the Alps. My father subsequently hinted to me that when the two young people showed signs of interest in each other, Hugo and Rosa exerted strong pressure on him to take things forward, and before long they were engaged. Martin, who had shown commercial gifts – he worked as an accountant in a firm owned by a relative of his sister Stefanie's husband – was offered a well-paid post as accountant in grandfather's company. Numerous letters from Else to Martin survive from the time of their courtship, and her intense and growing love is touchingly palpable.

In these letters, it is clear that Martin was highly resistant to being introduced to all Else's numberless relatives, while she was charmed by her warm reception by Martin's parents and sisters. Martin's eldest sister, Stefanie (born 1888) was already married and had a small son; I was given to understand that when Stefanie first met Else, she urged Martin to marry her, and a little while later – after their wedding – changed her opinion drastically. Perhaps it was because Stefanie's own marriage disintegrated about this time. Stefanie's opinions may have been changeable, but they were always strong.

I arrived fourteen months after the wedding, on 9 September 1924. I have reason to believe that my father quickly built up a head of steam resenting the way, as he saw it, he had been bulldozed into marriage. It cannot have helped at all that throughout the period 1923–1933, he and Else were obliged to live together with Else's parents (and later just Hugo). Hugo refused to have the accommodation converted into independent habitations, although my parents had asked for this to be done. Perhaps Rosa, my grandmother, insisted that she could not bear to have her surviving daughter out of her sight. My father began to use his newfound wealth to travel on sustained vacations, especially round the Mediterranean, leaving my mother behind to look after me.

I now recognize that my grandfather's ruthless insistence

that his daughter and her husband (and in due course, we children) should live with him, in two successive habitations in Fürth, had a devastating effect on my parents' marriage. Indeed, I am inclined to the view that this was the precipitating factor in my parents' marital crisis. It is clearly significant that from the time the family fled to Spain my grandfather lived separately, in a succession of hotels. It was only in his eighties, when he had become quite frail, that he once again lived with my mother. He must have learned, the hard way, the dangers of permanent cohabitation of different generations.*

I remember being taken on holiday by my mother alone, when I was quite small, to Switzerland at the beginning of August, when the Swiss national day is celebrated with a procession of coloured paper lanterns. My mother sought to limit my food intake, for I was rather greedy, and I defended myself by making good friends with the kitchen staff at our hotel. Even if I was not skilled at making friends with my own age-group, it seems that I was distinctly better able to build up relationships with older people, such as my Philitante. I had a nursemaid of whom I was fond – though I cannot now remember her name – and I also learnt a surprising amount from another maid. On one occasion when I was about five, this maid, while getting me ready for bed, told me an affecting tale about a French officer called Dreyfus, a Jew, who had been falsely accused and convicted of treason and sent to a hellhole of a jail in South America. She spoke of the fierce quarrels which erupted between foes and defenders of the wronged officer and how he was finally vindicated. I wept when I heard this story.

At about this time, I was sent to spend some weeks with my paternal grandparents in their spacious apartment in Munich. The maid here was a lot less obliging than the one

---

*The disastrous effect of forced permanent cohabitation of a husband and wife with – in this case – the husband's mother, on the state of that marriage, emerges very clearly from the well documented life of the Italian writer Primo Levi.

in Fürth. The Munich household, I discovered, had the unusual foible of using so-called 'vinegar essence' to prepare salad dressing; this was just concentrated acetic acid, to be diluted with water and mixed with oil. The maid told me with sadistic pleasure that the strong vinegar essence was a deadly poison and chased me through the apartment, waving the dangerous bottle. I fled, screaming. I sometimes wonder whether this was the origin of my reservations about chemistry as a suitable branch of science for me to embrace. Tiny events can have big effects.

One day in 1928, when I was not quite four, I was taken, without explanation, to the little Bavarian town of Landshut, some distance from Fürth, and there left in the charge of a childminder. The childminder was apt to wedge me in a chair, hard up against a table, from which I could not escape, and leave me to my own devices with a few toy cars. It was a terrible few weeks. Then someone came to retrieve me, and when we reached home, I was taken into a bedroom where my grandfather, father and mother were drawn up in an expectant half-circle; my mother had a small doll in her arms. Clearly I was expected to say something, so I asked, 'Where are my toys?' That evening, it seems, I emptied some ink over my newborn sister, Irene, in her cradle. That was the first of many dislocations in my life.

I think it was not till we were together in Pitar Ray's school, five years later, that Irene and I really began to get on well. We shared an interest in dressing up, and we also became obsessed with languages – we were both learning new ones left and right – and acquired the habit of speaking to each other in wild linguistic mixtures: a novel kind of fraternal/sororal secret language. Eventually, after the War was over, Irene studied the art of interpreting in Geneva.

In the summer of 1930, when I was approaching the age of six, the family moved from our flat in the centre of Fürth to the new villa in the suburbs. Almost at once, I began my schooling, at the primary school in the village of Dambach, only half a mile or so from our new home. I walked the distance daily, both ways; it was not then thought dangerous for a six-year-old to take such walks alone. On the first day, each of us beginners was given a large conical container of assorted sweets to console us for our lost freedom. However, I apparently protested vigorously at home that evening because the teacher had instructed us to sit on our seats quietly, with our hands flat on our desks! I was fortunate to be well taught and it took me very little time to learn reading and writing. The only book which I can now recall being given by my parents to read in my seventh or eighth year was the collected fairy tales of Wilhelm Hauff, oriental tales with some resemblance to *The Arabian Nights*. I think my mother must have read some of the Grimm fairy tales to me, as well as the more respectable tales from *The Arabian Nights*; also the adventures of Struwwelpeter and of Max and Moritz, because I remember those too, but don't remember having read them myself. I particularly cherished the story about the boy who set out to find the meaning of terror (the expressive German word in the story is 'gruseln'), and nothing worked until someone poured a bucketful of cold fish down the inside of his shirt. That was perhaps why, twenty-two years later at Birmingham University, I was so greatly taken with the phrase used by a professor's eccentric wife: '...better than a slap in the belly with a wet fish.' This has been part of our family vocabulary for decades. Somewhat later, not long before we left Germany, I found and read a German school story about a Valkyrie-like schoolgirl. But that is all the reading-matter I can remember until I reached Pitar Ray's school at the age of nine and my acquaintance with literature took off.

There came a time – I believe it was in late 1932 – when I began to be bullied at school and yelled at as a dirty Jew, both by some of my schoolfellows and by older boys who shouted through the school railings. My teacher did not do anything like this, but he did not have the courage to reprove the bullies. I was also, one day, stopped from swimming in the local river, because that was 'not for Jews'. At this point my parents and grandfather took alarm; no physical violence had yet been used against me, but that was likely to be next. So I was sent to a boarding school in the Black Forest, belonging to a delightful ex-officer, a Major Kohlermann. The months in this school were idyllic – lessons interspersed with afternoons when we children collected mushrooms in the forest, or acted as beaters for the Major, who was a passionate hunter. I must have been happy at this school, because for the only time in my life I won an award for good behaviour. The award entitled me to choose an evening meal of my preference: I chose Wiener Schnitzel with potato and cucumber salads, and wolfed down nine plates of cucumber salad! I still cannot resist this combination of dishes. It was from this school that my father collected me in the summer of 1933 when he took me to Switzerland.

As my parents' marriage began to disintegrate, my mother began to practise sculpture under the guidance of Karl Boessenecker. By the time I was six, she had made considerable progress, and in a letter to a friend written in 1930 she described her activities, including a commission to model an acquaintance's head. Her sculpting must have impressed me, though I cannot now remember any of her works, because in that letter, she quotes me as saying that I intended to become an artist, painting four days a week, sculpting two days – and spending the remaining day as a business man, like papa.

My father had three sisters: in sequence, Stefanie, Marie and Johanna (known as Hansi). Stefanie married Martin Feuchtwanger, brother of the renowned Jewish novelist Lion Feuchtwanger, and had one son, Klaus (born 1912). Through her marriage, Stefanie became closely involved with German literary circles. Her husband began to engage in affairs, and Stefanie, less tolerant than my mother, soon separated from him. Her powerful emotions centred on little Klaus, who became extremely self-absorbed; when in 1929 I was sent to visit my aunt in Berlin, Klaus, then aged eighteen, was intensely jealous of any attention his mother paid me, and this jealousy lasted throughout the remaining fifty-two years of his life, most of which were spent in America.

It may have been my difficulties with Klaus that helped to move me, for some years in middle life, to steer clear of my many surviving elder relatives, especially those who had taken refuge in America; having done my utmost to become as English as I could, I felt uncomfortable with those of my seniors who had remained very 'continental' in personality. But I am glad to say that I overcame this unworthy impulse after a while.

Marie's marriage also disintegrated soon; she had no children.

Hansi, the baby of the Cahn family and a great charmer, had one daughter, Margot. My paternal grandparents were deeply concerned to know what they had done to lead three of their children into such marital disasters; if they reached a conclusion, I don't know what it was.

I think that it was as a small child, before we ever left Germany, that I decided with fierce resolve that my marriage, when it eventually came, was going to last, and that it was going to be a real marriage. Apparently I told my mother smugly that my wife should certainly be beautiful, if fortune smiled on me, but in any case she should be good. Lessons learnt from the disasters of others can sometimes guide one's life to very good effect. In due course, after a cautiously prolonged – too prolonged – courtship, I married a woman who, indeed, was both beautiful and good.

3

England

My father – whom I now took to calling 'poppa' – collected me at Croydon Airport and drove me to his apartment in St John's Wood on the far side of London. That district, together with neighbouring Swiss Cottage, was crammed with Jewish refugees like ourselves. Poppa lived in a small apartment in a block on Abbey Road, and, with a business partner, had established himself as a wholesale merchant, buying handbag frames and small mirrors and selling them on to makers of handbags. His office was deep in the City of London. Things appeared to be going quite well.

Poppa had decided to send me to a boys' boarding school, even though that would be far more expensive than a day school. He clearly did not think that, in the absence of my mother, he could cope with me living at home the year round. He did not, of course, understand the English school system, and decided to take the advice of a Hungarian immigrant friend who, as I came to realize, understood that system even less. The school, Maiden Erlegh, near Reading, was in a palatial mansion originally built for a South African mining tycoon, in a spacious estate on the outskirts of Reading, within easy reach of London. The tycoon had used the mansion for uproarious parties during which ladies of the night were thrown into the swimming-pool, and the school still contained dim echoes of those occasions. The headmaster was an antediluvian military man, Captain Waterlow-Fox, and, as I was to discover, it was a place of little academic quality. I came bouncing in somewhat boastfully, rather like a twelve-year-old Tigger, in the Winnie-the-Pooh stories, claiming, quite untruthfully, to be good at football. I was very quickly put in my place by the school bullies, of whom there was never any shortage, and who were encouraged by the headmaster to keep my bounciness at bay. There was nothing about the school that would have encouraged me to make friends, that activity in which I was so unskilled. I never told poppa what was happening to me at the school, or what I thought of the place.

Fifteen years later, I attended a scientific meeting in Reading and afterwards, on an impulse, drove out to Maiden Erlegh. I found it in the process of being demolished to make way for a housing estate. The lawns were covered in fitments to be auctioned off; I performed a dance of triumph between the lavatory bowls and bathroom taps.

There were two memorably good teachers: Miss Taylor (English) and Mr Mellor (history), while another, Mr Mandy, did a good job of repairing my fractured Spanish. Mr Piper, who taught French, had an enjoyable line in deep eccentricity. The rest of the staff did little to earn their salaries. I recall a splendid series of lessons on *The Merchant of Venice* which, as may be imagined, spoke eloquently to me. The headmaster judged that I was bright and told me that I should prepare to take School Certificate – the normal school-leaving examination of the time, usually taken at sixteen – two years after my arrival, when I would be not quite fourteen, and this I duly did, with respectable results in spite of my absurd youth. I recall an oral examiner who came round to interview candidates who offered foreign languages. His expression, when he saw me for the third time the same day because I was offering three foreign languages, is something I still remember with amusement. My German-language essay in that examination was a panegyric to freedom and tolerance, so, in spite of my unhappiness at the school, I had clearly somehow seen and absorbed enough of the essential nature of English life to have become devoted to it very quickly.

The head boy that year was a twenty-year-old who had not yet taken the School Certificate but he was registered to take the plunge that summer. He was afraid of the examination and did not turn up. However, he remained head boy, presumably because he came from a rich family.

While all this was going on, poppa made valiant attempts to give me his company and comfort. He would come round on a Saturday and take me to an inn in Sonning-on-Thames for a genteel tea with thin cucumber sandwiches and delicate slices of madeira cake. When I was home on vacation, he would at intervals take me out to news cinemas, institutions which no longer exist, to show me something of what was going on in the world. Not long after I had arrived in England, he and his current lady friend – I think at her instigation – took me to a splendid London performance of *Macbeth*, with Gwen Ffrangcon-Davies as Lady Macbeth. It moved me intensely. That was my first exposure to high art in public performance, and I am still grateful to poppa for that crucial experience.* The school only took me to plays like *1066 and All That*. A little later poppa also formed the habit of taking me to London art galleries, particularly the National Gallery and the Wallace Collection, and talking to me about some of the pictures; that also had a lasting effect. About music, I will write later.

In the summer holidays, poppa drove me to the continent. In France, on one occasion, he took me to see a portion of the surviving trench system of the First World War, in which he had been a machine-gunner sergeant for the Kaiser and spoke feelingly about the nature of war. In 1937 we drove

---

*I believe that I recall the name of the actress who played Lady Macbeth, but not that of the actor who played Macbeth himself, because I was so struck by the immensely villainous Lady as well as the three ferocious witches. Even at my tender age, since I knew something about the Nazis, abominable men did not surprise me, but the women were something else again. This was also the first time that I learned that great poetry coud make tragedy uplifting as well as terrifying. I think I must have been purged by pity and terror, as the classical phrase has it.

over dizzy alpine passes in Switzerland to visit my other relatives in northern Italy. My father was always punctilious about encouraging me to maintain contact with my mother and sister and never troubled me by speaking ill of my mother; she reciprocated this impressive courtesy, for which, in retrospect, I am deeply grateful.

I did not regularly read newspapers then and had only an indistinct awareness of the desperate politics of that time. When Neville Chamberlain returned from Munich, waving that notorious scrap of paper and declaring 'peace in our time', our headmaster gave us a half-day's holiday in celebration. That met the general mood of the day.

When I returned to the school in the autumn of 1938, I had to find something to do. A new English scholar had come to supplement the existing one, and he created a kind of miniature advanced class for me in which he tried to teach me English literature beyond that to which I had already been exposed. However, he knew nothing about teaching, and when, without any explanation of context, he gave me Cardinal Newman's very difficult *Apologia pro Vita Sua* to read and comment on, I decided that this sort of thing was not for me. So, gingerly, I attended classes in physics and chemistry, as well as advanced mathematics. All three were taught indifferently: advanced maths by another scholar who did not know how to teach, physics by a failed medical student who used a good deal of the class time to sow cynical political ideas in our minds (and in 1938–1940, there was plenty to be cynical about), while chemistry was taught by an older man who had been a soldier and had suffered shell-shock in the First World War. In spite of the fact that he was eccentric to the point of lunacy, he had some didactic ability and I recall being fascinated by the periodic table. He would not, however, have met the requirements of today's health and safety at work regulations. He encouraged me, for example, to make chlorine from manganese dioxide and hydrochloric acid, watching me from outside the laboratory, through the window, as I did so. I added the acid too fast and when I got a whiff of chlorine in my lungs and spent half an hour coughing it away, he giggled nervously but did nothing.

In the early summer of 1940, I took School Certificate again in my three new subjects, and again did well, in spite of the dubious teaching I had received. I early learnt to teach myself from textbooks.

Meanwhile, the War had begun. Some time in the June of 1940, the headmaster summoned me and informed me that poppa had been interned in the panic of that month, together with a majority of German and Austrian Jewish refugees, when a Nazi invasion was daily expected. Winston Churchill had given the instruction, 'Collar the lot!' Soon after, the last day of term came and I reached a decision: I informed the headmaster that I would not be returning to Maiden Erlegh in the autumn and that I would be seeking out a day school in London which would enable me to reach university. So far as I was aware, no-one had ever managed that from Maiden Erlegh direct. He was too shocked by my impudence to try to argue. I was not yet sixteen, and 'enemy aliens' were not at risk of internment until they reached this age.

Before his internment, poppa had moved to a more spacious apartment, still in St John's Wood; it was on the ground floor of a skyscraper and poppa reckoned that we were marginally less likely to be killed by a bomb in that location. Now that he was interned – first on the Isle of Man, subsequently in the Lancashire village of Huyton – I was decanted into a lodging in Swiss Cottage, where I lived on my own. Meanwhile, the Nazi aerial bombardment of London – the Blitz – increased in its fury and the Spitfires and Hurricanes of the Royal Air Force fought the Battle of Britain which saved us all from invasion that summer and which reached its apogee in the middle of August. I soon found a grammar school, Haberdasher Aske's School, where I was accepted to study advanced sciences. After I had been there for a few weeks, although I was very happy there, my father in his internment learnt about the fury of the Blitz and became desperately alarmed for me. He wrote and begged Lil, his current mistress and a delightful lady, to take me out of London to somewhere safer, and, after another few weeks of grammar school and of bombs, including a very near miss, in late September Lil and I set out for the Lake District. Someone had told Lil that this was a quiet corner of the land. We stayed in a small hotel in Buttermere and I began looking for a school. The famous Keswick School in the little town of that name would not accept me, so I turned west and found a 'technical school' in the grimy industrial town of Workington, where the headmaster was happy to have me. We boarded in a private house. Lil soon became bored by the calmness of life there and, since the Blitz had abated considerably, returned to the fleshpots of London, leaving me to my own devices in Workington. I assured her that I would be perfectly all right. In the autumn, poppa was freed, together with the great majority of the internees, and was happily reunited with Lil. Soon he came to visit me in Workington and we went off on a tremendous mountain walk together over the Lakeland fells. Unfortunately, about this time there was a resurgence of the Blitz and poppa's offices in the City were destroyed; thereafter, he moved to an office in Swiss Cottage, near his home and, after the War, to the West End of London.

Meanwhile, I took classes in physics, chemistry, advanced mathematics, mechanics and technical drawing, all of unmistakably high quality, and enjoyed myself thoroughly. I learnt a few not terribly profitable things, such as the geometrical design of valvegear for steam locomotives – but even that was fun. At this school, I also began to make friends and became a devoted mountaineer.

I was interviewed by a panel in Preston, to determine whether I was safe to leave at liberty or should be interned, now I was sixteen. Happily they decided that the safety of the realm would not be gravely endangered by my continued liberty.

At Maiden Erlegh, the only rôle model I had encountered had been Miss Taylor, the English teacher; in Workington, all the teachers taught me memorable things. Thus, the chemistry teacher warned his class eloquently about the perils of self-pity, especially at examination time; this persuasive warning has been a particular boon to me over the years. The physics teacher gave me my first true experience of quantitative rigour; and the mechanics teacher at one point entreated me to '...be a Christian and give someone else a chance', to which I responded, 'But sir, I am not a Christian!' – but I did give someone else a chance.

I admired various girls from afar – and two from a little closer. One of these, Queenie, turned out to be an agreeable companion on mountain expeditions. One especially pretty girl, a tall strawberry blonde, appealed particularly; but since she was the daughter of the local police chief and I was an 'enemy alien' I hardly dared to speak to her. Yet another looked (disconcertingly, in retrospect) like the woman I would eventually marry and I longed for her attention, but did not get it.

In my second year at the school, in 1941–42, it was time to decide on a university. As an enemy alien, the only military service I would have been allowed to perform would have entailed digging latrines and the like. As I shall explain below, my choice fell on Cambridge University, and my performance in the Higher School Certificate, taken at the end of my two years in Workington, turned out to be quite sufficient. To enter, however, I needed a formal qualification in Latin. So, in early 1942, just before the end of my schooling, I found a private tutor to give me six weeks' tuition in elementary Latin – I had forgotten the bit of Latin I had learnt in Barcelona – and that sufficed to get me the piece of paper I needed to qualify. It was a source of solid satisfaction that at the outset the tutor had thrown up his hands in horror and assured me I would be wasting my money studying Latin for only six weeks. I pointed out that it was my money and I could waste it if I wished. As I have remarked before, tact was not my strong point in my youth.

These two years, divided between the grime of Workington and the limpid beauty of the Lake District fells, and darkened by the worst years of a desperate War, constituted my first period of unalloyed youthful happiness.

In 1942, I had to decide finally on a subject for my university degree. I am convinced that such choices can stem from absurdly small events. Some time in 1938 or 1939 when I was fourteen and just beginning in science, a friend of poppa's who was a professional metallurgist took me along to a scientific meeting at the Institute of Metals in London. I enjoyed the lecture, though I have entirely forgotten what it was about, but I remember clearly the luscious array of cakes and buns available for the taking afterwards. Any profession which could look after the inner man so effectively must, I thought, be worth taking seriously. So, by 1942, it had come down to a choice between metallurgy and mining engineering. This last, I thought misguidedly, would entail some delectable travel in beautiful mountainous regions. Metallurgy eventually won my heart, but neither poppa nor I knew anything much about appropriate universities. I had heard of Sheffield and of Imperial College in London, but that was as far as it went.

At this point yet another 'small event' intervened, and this was the direct precursor of my advanced education and also of my very happy marriage. My father had developed the habit of organising, in his apartment in London, string quartet evenings, involving a mix of professional and amateur musicians. He ranged far and wide in locating good instrumentalists; he himself played the viola. In early 1942, he invited the violinist wife of Tressilian Nicholas, the senior bursar of Trinity College, Cambridge, to join one of these evenings. She duly came with her husband in tow and, during the 'half-time' meal, my father asked Tressilian, who was a geologist by training, about where his eccentric son might with advantage go to study metallurgy. He replied that he understood that Cambridge had, a few years before the War, introduced metallurgy as a speciality in the Natural Sciences Tripos and that the professor, one Robert Hutton, was known to be well disposed to German Jewish refugees. Tressilian further undertook to act as a go-between and arrange an interview with Professor Hutton. He told me that if that went well I should feel free to apply to Trinity for a place in the autum of that same year. (Undergraduate admissions were, and are, exclusively the concern of the colleges, not of the academic departments of the university or of the university centrally.)

The outcome was that, a few weeks later, poppa and I took a train to Cambridge to meet Professor Hutton. We were early and found the Copper Kettle, a café on King's Parade in the centre of Cambridge, where we spent the time till we were due. We sat by a window on the first floor, gazing at the extraordinary view of King's College Chapel and the stone 'screens' fronting King's College. Poppa told me later that, after a spell of absorbing this truly remarkable architectural sight, I turned to him and said fervently, 'This is going to be my university.' Hutton was indeed very encouraging when I told him of my scientific record to date and his attitude gave me the confidence to apply to Trinity College. When my Higher School Certificate results were published in the summer and I had passed my simple Latin test, Trinity informed me that they were happy to take me. That automatically gave me the entrée to the various science departments, including metallurgy.

Nearly forty years later, when my wife and I were living in Lewes, East Sussex, very near the Glyndebourne Opera House, I had the notion of inviting Tressilian Nicholas, then in his nineties, retired from the Trinity bursarship and long widowered, to be our guest at a performance of Mozart's *Magic Flute* at Glyndebourne, as thanks for his pregnant advice all those years before. He came, full of life and energy, said that he had always wanted to see a performance of this opera and enjoyed himself enormously. I reminded him of what he had done for me, but when he returned to College, he told his friends wonderingly about the extraordinary gift he had been given – he had already forgotten the reason for it. However, a few years later, having retired to Cambridge, we were invited to his hundredth birthday party.

4

University

I began my time at Trinity College as a student of Natural Sciences in October 1942. Initially I was housed in rooms not far away, which was common in those days, but thereafter in college. Many academic staff were away on war service of one kind or another and undergraduates were left much to their own devices. I spoke with my director of studies once, for five minutes or so, and that was that. However, the crucial Cambridge practice of 'supervising' undergraduates, weekly, in small groups, typically groups of two, was maintained in the face of all staffing difficulties and I quickly came to perceive the merits of that custom.

The fact that I was, formally, an 'enemy alien', had no overt influence at all on the way I was treated by the college, though I suspect that it contributed to my sense of being slightly on the edge of many things. I never became close to any of the college fellows; even my personal tutor kept his distance and I only saw him a very few times. But I settled into university life at once, and smoothly, and so I found that I did not need counselling. I had had independence thrust upon me early in life, and that stood me in very good stead.

My director of studies arranged for me to attend lectures, and mostly be supervised, in five disciplines: physics, chemistry, mathematics, metallurgy and mineralogy. These subjects, jointly, made up my course for Part I of the Natural Sciences

Tripos,* to be examined in a dry run at the end of the first year, and in earnest at the end of the second year. My great discovery was mineralogy, taught in a department with several outstanding staff but very few undergraduates specialising in the subject. Most of the department's effort, therefore, went into teaching people like me who were planning to specialise in something else. In essence, the mineralogy course was devoted to crystallography, including x-ray diffraction, crystal chemistry and crystal physics and optics, together with a purely notional element of formal determinative study of minerals. The study in quantitative depth of crystals, a Cambridge speciality as I found out much later, was an intellectual revelation for me and shaped my eventual career in research.

The introductory course in metallurgy during the first two years was less than inspiring, much of it being purely descriptive, but the subject livened up considerably in the final year which was wholly devoted to the study of my chosen speciality, culminating in an examination for Part 2 of the Natural Sciences Tripos at the end of the third year.

For anyone who has not been an undergraduate at Cambridge or Oxford, it is quite difficult to appreciate the distinct roles of college and university. One is admitted to a college (a prospective student was free to apply to several colleges) to 'read' a particular discipline, or within a group of disciplines like 'natural sciences'. The college organises the small-group supervisions, but lectures and laboratory work are entirely the function of university departments. Most of the 'dons' who give lectures on behalf of a university department are also college fellows, and in that capacity give supervisions. Examinations are prepared and marked by the university. A student's fees are divided between his college and the university. Some colleges (like Trinity) are very rich, others are poor, but

---

* 'Tripos' is the venerable Cambridge name for an entire course and its associated examinations; it derives from the three-legged stool on which one of the oral examiners was wont to sit.

the rich colleges quietly give considerable help to the impoverished ones. It is complicated, but in the main it all works smoothly.

One college fellow whom I did unexpectedly meet was the Master of Trinity, the eminent historian George Macaulay Trevelyan. He was also a renowned mountain walker, capable of astonishing feats of endurance in his youth, and he must have been intrigued by a mountaineering poem of mine which won a college award. He invited me to lunch, together with a diplomat guest, in the Master's Lodge. He turned out to be strikingly shy and the conversation was left largely to the diplomat and myself; but I had a sense of being in the presence of a great man such as I have never had before or since.

The college provides living accommodation and meals. Today, many students prefer to cook for themselves, but with wartime rationing that would not have been feasible. The huge dining hall at Trinity was overlooked by a copy of a Holbein portrait of Henry VIII, and above that was the college motto: 'Semper eadem'. Those words, meaning 'always the same things', described the food on offer in wartime with admirable terseness, but at least we were able to buy beer to go with the meals. I supplemented the college diet with unrationed 'doughcakes' and chelsea buns from Fitzbillies, a bakery shop in the middle of town; I can still smell, in my mind's nose, the mouthwatering spicy scent of the doughcakes. Fitzbillies is still going strong today, but the doughcakes have vanished.

I have said nothing as yet in these memoirs about sport, except for my fatal boastfulness at school concerning my non-existent prowess as a goalkeeper. This is because, mountaineering apart, I have no sporting talent. When I lived in San Cugat in Spain, at the edge of a private golf course, a friendly neighbour gave me one club (a number three wood) and a couple of golf balls as an eleventh birthday present, and I immediately began to trespass on the golf course in the middle of the day, when it was too hot for most of the members. No-one explained that a golfer needs a range of different clubs, and no-one offered me any lessons, and I did everything, including putting, with that solitary wood; the putting was somewhat hindered by the fact that the 'greens' were actually composed of oiled sand. At intervals the golf club secretary would see me and chase me off with firm words. Perhaps I recalled that my nickname at that time was Robert the Devil, and I must have known the dictum that one chases out the devil with a pitchfork but he always comes running back, so as soon as the secretary was out of view I would be back on the course. I became fond of golf and played it from time to time as an adult, but I never learnt it properly. That was not the only problem, however; simple lack of talent played its rôle too. When, many years later, I took my sixteen-year-old son Andrew, who is very athletic, on to the Queen's Course at Gleneagles, in Scotland, his very first time with a golf club in his hands he beat me convincingly. At Cambridge I did not have the resources to attempt membership of a golf club, so I kept fit by cross-country running; I usually came in last, but that did not worry me. Later on I played squash, again trespassing, in the squash court of St John's College next door, because Trinity did not have a squash court.

In 1993, at the age of sixty-nine I spent three months as a visiting professor at a university near San Cugat, and took the chance to play several rounds on the golf course where I had trespassed as a child. Now the greens were of the finest grass, prepared to perfection – which is more than I can say for my golf technique.

Both the University and my College offered the chance to join numerous societies, which flourished in spite of the extreme academic pressure at a time when most students had only two years in Cambridge before being called up for some form of military or research service. My favourite society was the mountaineering club. The political societies were virtually closed down for the duration of the War – after all, Britain was governed throughout the War by a coalition government – but a wartime organisation had been created to replace them, the Cambridge University Society for International

Affairs, CUSIA for short. CUSIA arranged talks by politicians and diplomats from many countries who were caught in wartime England and this gave students some sense of the great world outside, now inaccessible to travel. The Society also had a social side and arranged film showings. I joined this body enthusiastically and after a while I became joint secretary, together with Sonia Lechem, another student of metallurgy, who is my oldest surviving friend today. My future wife was actively involved on the social side.

In College I joined the chess club and played – and was regularly beaten by – such luminaries as the future mathematics professor, James Lighthill. I also enjoyed the antics of the College debating society, 'The Magpie and Stump', so called because its emblem was a stuffed magpie sitting on a small tree stump, which had to be on display whenever the society was in session. 'The Magpie and Stump' was relentlessly jocular, debating with mock earnestness motions such as: 'That men are clay, and women make mugs of them'. The atmosphere of its meetings was reminiscent of *Alice in Wonderland*, and so it was no wonder that it appealed particularly to mathematicians such as James Lighthill, who was one of the society's presidents.

I wrote frequently to my mother and sister in their Spanish exile, of necessity in German, and mother responded with equal frequency. Between us, we gave the postal censor a good deal of work to do. That link maintained by paper encouraged me to travel to Spain soon after the War to re-establish proper personal contact.

Friendships at last came my way, especially within the College. One such friend, Michael Bell, a student of modern languages, had a room above mine in College. At one stage he was pursuing a delectable tall girl from Newnham, Daphne Meier, who insisted on attending parties, whenever feasible, jointly with her best friend, Patricia Hanson; both were first-year students of English Literature, newly arrived in Cambridge. So one day in November 1943, early in my own second year, when I was nineteen, Michael invited me to help him entertain

41

this pair of girls in his room; essentially my rôle was to absorb the attention of Pat, who was not quite eighteen, while Michael exercised his wiles (unsuccessfully) on Daphne. This diversionary task proved highly enjoyable. Pat squatted comfortably at my feet and listened attentively to my tales of rock-climbing. It soon transpired that she was a newly hatched climber herself; her father had recently taken her up various routes in North Wales. To adopt a convenient Spanish term, I found Pat 'muy simpatica', and I did not, it seemed, bore her unduly. Pat's own memory of that evening in Michael Bell's room, and what followed, expressed fifty-six years later in the course of an after-dinner speech she gave at a scientific conference which chanced to coincide with my seventy-fifth birthday, was as follows:

I first met Robert in November 1943 at Cambridge, after a meeting on politics. I and my closest girl friend Daphne were invited for coffee by her current suitor, and there was Robert. I won his approval by, literally, sitting at his feet and listening to his exploits on a rope. My father had recently taken me up three climbs in North Wales. Robert had already been climbing for several years, and enjoyed talking to a fellow enthusiast. His willingness to encourage possible talent, and his characteristic optimism in the face of the impractical, emerged in his trying to introduce me to the all-male Cambridge Mountaineering Club. They at least recognised that I was female and rejected me. As a substitute he took me to concerts, as he thought my musical education had been neglected and he enjoyed the generous transmission of knowledge. I liked his conversation and recognised an interesting and capacious mind. I didn't consider him brilliant, as there were occasions when he was a little slow on the uptake – and not only in taking eighteen months to notice that I was a girl. By the time he did I had forgotten that he was a man, so we took a little time to get adjusted. But we were always friends. As well as music and mountaineering we shared an interest in literature and words, and Robert made me aware of the links and differences between languages, and the way in which a language expresses the character of a nation.

Two and a half years later we finally became engaged, and were married not quite four years after that first meeting. I had indeed found a wife who was both beautiful and good, and we embarked on a life together which was everything I could ever have hoped for.

Reflecting on this first meeting and the slow courtship that followed, I am much struck by the fact that, during my last two years at school, and subsequently in Cambridge, I had light romantic attachments to a number of girls, but I cannot remember how and where I first met any of them. My first meeting with Pat is, however, firmly lodged in my memory.

When I came up to Cambridge, there were only two people in residence whom I already knew. One was a fellow-pupil at the Workington school who was a year above me, but my acquaintance with him was very slight. The other was my second cousin, Ernst Sondheimer. He and his younger brother Franz, direct descendants of Veit Weil, were both notable young scientists, Ernst being a physicist and his brother a renowned organic chemist who later became closely involved with the research leading to the development of the first contraceptive pill – and, as a result, very wealthy. Ernst was a scholar at Trinity College, again a year ahead of me. Being a scholar, in those days, implied success in a special, very demanding examination set by the college, not by an external public body; a scholar did in fact receive a small amount of financial aid but, more importantly, he was part of a college élite, allocated a fine suite of rooms, invited to various celebration dinners and generally regarded as a top dog. Ernst was well aware of this and in those days he was inclined to look down his nose at me. I had never attempted the scholarship examination for my school had never told me of its existence! So Ernst was not in practice a close friend, although nowadays we get on perfectly affably. Ernst's brother had a meteoric career, down as well as up, and eventually in a fit of deep depression took his own life. Ernst did some highly distinguished research in theoretical solid-state physics, became a college research fellow at Trinity and, in due course, went on to a notable career in British academic life, as well as becoming an influential member of the Alpine Club in London.

There may have been no ready-made friends for me, but I got to know numerous students of both sexes in a range of colleges, including of course Trinity. One with whom I have remained on terms of friendship for over sixty years is Freeman Dyson, the charismatic mathematician, physicist and writer, one of the brightest scholars who ever graced Trinity, who overlapped with me. He has for many years worked at the Institute for Advanced Study in Princeton, where he made his name with his researches on quantum electrodynamics. He is also famous now as a populariser of science. I am immensely indebted to him for writing a lively Foreword to this book.

Another friend was Twum-Barima, a self-confident black aristocrat from the Gold Coast who was studying agriculture and delighted all his friends by using his wit to demolish an acerbic Member of Parliament who sought to slight him. Later in life he was very badly treated by the corrupt Ghanaian government. Johnny Thatcher, a Scottish student of English Literature who had rooms adjacent to mine, was a delightful, sunny man who used to disturb the peace of Great Court with his bagpipes, and we had all the usual conversations about life, liberty and the pursuit of happiness, fuelled by coffee – malt whisky not being to hand. In due course, Johnny took a strong fancy to Pat, who was by that stage my fiancée. She was fond of him too. Johnny was a frequent visitor. One occasion when Pat came to see me in my rooms in Great Court an observant college porter intercepted her with the words, 'Mr Cahn isn't in just now, but Mr Thatcher is in his room'. There was not much the college porters did not know about the students. Johnny was my best man at my wedding to Pat in 1947. He himself married another charming girl and had a son, but then was sent to Karachi by his employer, where he caught polio and died. Pat and I miss him still.

Pat and I, and Pat's friend Daphne, took part in setting up a play-reading group which met frequently, both in my room and elsewhere, and through this we became acquainted with a number of amateur actors at Trinity College, some of whom in later life became professionals. These people were extremely self-absorbed, as well as being witty and good company some of the time, and I learnt a good deal about the psychology of actors and the nature of theatre. Cambridge at that time was blessed with wondrous performances of plays by Shakespeare and other early playwrights given by the Marlowe Society, under the genial guidance of actor, scholar and director George (Dadie) Rylands. Pat and I soon learnt about the gulf fixed between outstanding productions on the stage, and all the rest.

In the summer of 1944 I had completed two years at Cambridge and was thus subject to direction of labour. I was interviewed by a civil servant who later became famous in another sphere, C.P. Snow. He decided that as an enemy alien I could not be recruited into secret research and that my record was good enough to allow me to stay on for a third year, an uncommon privilege at that time. I decided to stay with my choice of metallurgy as a specialist theme, though I could have transferred, for instance, to physics. I recall some exciting lectures, given by a scholar, David Stockdale, who had been recalled from retirement, about elementary statistical mechanics and order-disorder transitions in alloys. These made such an impression on me that, ten years later, I chose such transitions as a major theme of my own research.

In early May 1945, the Allies achieved victory in Europe, and a few days later my final examinations for the bachelor's degree began. The evening of the day on which victory was announced every town and village in Britain celebrated vigorously in the streets, and church bells were rung loudly. VE day really had for me a quite special resonance, enabling me to feel for the first time in twelve years that my close family and I were at last quite safe from murder by the Nazis.

In the event, my degree was respectable – good enough to qualify me to undertake research for a doctoral degree. I discussed this ambition with Professor Hutton. The research studentship I was offered at the Cavendish Laboratory, financed by a steel research organization, brought in £225 per annum, which in those days was enough to live on, with care and some frugality.

So, in the summer of 1945, my formal education was at last over, at the age of almost twenty-one, but my informal scientific education was just beginning.

5

Mountains and Marriage

In the preceding chapters, I have in passing mentioned my deep love of mountains. Although I cannot begin to claim status as a 'tiger', as highly athletic and skilled alpinists are sometimes called, nevertheless many of my happiest hours have been spent among rocks and hills.

My son Martin recently uncovered on the internet an article I wrote for *Cambridge Mountaineering*, the magazine of the Cambridge University Mountaineering Club which taught me much of what I know about rock-climbing. The article, which I had totally forgotten, appeared in 1944, when I was twenty. I cannot do better than quote some extracts from it, since it represents the spontaneous and emotional reactions of a very young man:

It began early. Ever since leaving Germany as a small boy, a fugitive from the Führer, I have been surrounded by all sorts of mountains; that is probably the only thing I have to thank the Führer for. The first were the cliffs and hills of Majorca, an island where the most varied beauties of hill, plain and shore are compressed into a space of a few square miles. When we had been set free from the schoolroom some hot summer afternoon, a pack of us, wearing only shorts and a pair of alpargatas (light canvas shoes with rope soles which everyone in these parts wears) would rush out over the parched heath towards the fresh air of the seashore and the cliffs. And what adventures we had among them, those fantastic lime-stone shapes, their features wrinkled by wind and sea into countless corrugations which the alpargatas gripped with delightful firmness; with their great mysterious caves, in which the breakers boomed resonantly over stolid ranks of sea-hedgehogs and other queer-shaped creatures. This was the training ground where I first learnt to climb with all four extremities... There was one particularly large cave, with a chimney at the far end; you climbed up this, and suddenly you emerged from the cold clammy recess on to a sun-baked plateau high above the sea. It was a new surprise every time we did it... But the Spanish sun in summer has little in common with its feeble counterpart of more northerly latitudes, and soon we would be scampering off again to the shelter of our caves.

All that was in 1933–35. A few years later, in 1940, when I was taken to the Lake District to avoid the bombs in London, I had my next formative experience:

A kindly walker took me up the Guide's Route to Scafell Pike, the highest of them all; this is a fine mountaineering route, winding its way up the mountain's flank to land one on the boulder-strewn summit plateau... It is a remarkable fact that the bare stark nature of many of the Lake District hilltops lends them a peculiar attractive-ness. Perhaps it is due to the part they play in furnishing another contrast in a land already rich in contrasts: steep rock face against blue lakes and grey rocks; and the most obvious contrast of all, the ceaseless changing of the weather.

Rock-climbing came next, initially in the company of a friend from my Workington school and then with members of the Cambridge Club:

I had always thought of rock-climbers as very superior

48

persons who were on another plane altogether from us humble walkers, until one day I found myself gaily scaling the vertical side of Pillar Rock [*above Ennerdale in the Lake District*] with a sangfroid I should have shuddered at a year before. This New West Climb really does merit the attention of all climbers, from the trembling novice to the most hardened veteran bred in the tradition of de Selincourtian gravity defiance [*here I was showing off my familiarity with rock-climbing history*]. It has plenty of exposure and sensational positions, it is steep in the most modern meaning of the word, and in its three hundred feet or so of continuous climbing it calls for all types of technique. It starts with a 'staircase', traverses off the 'landing' to a steep groove, soon after which the climber can spreadeagle himself on a step even wider than the notorious Stride on the North Climb. Then follows a beautiful chimney, complete with chockstone, and topped by a wicked vice which most people attempt the first time they do the climb, in the mistaken belief that the route continues up it. As a matter of fact, it emerges from the chimney to follow a traverse which is almost completely hidden from the climber inside the chimney. This traverse is not lavish with its handholds, and gives exhilarating balance climbing. Finally there is a dose of good smooth slabs, which take one right out on to the summit of the Rock. The sort of perfect climb that a valley-bound cragsman might compose for the solace of his imagination, as a gourmet on a desert island might conjure up visions of the perfect meal. And yet withal it is easy enough, unless of course it happens to be raining.

Today the tigers would consider that climb so absurdly undemanding that it would barely warrant a passing mention in a guidebook.

At about the same time as I wrote that essay, I wrote a poem for a verse competition in my Cambridge College, called simply *The Climb*. It began with the same theme, the 'valley-bound cragsman' yearning to be in the mountains, and went on in highly romantic form to describe a climb, the New West Climb as it might have been. Here are a few lines from the poem (which won the Enoch Powell Award for English Verse at Trinity College):

At first the foot mistrusts its unaccustomed perch,
And timid hand creeps doubting o'er the rough-hewn
   stone.
But not for long; the foot becomes more bold
And firmer fingers grasp each jutting hold.
There's no above, below; no future, past ... We are alone
In the whole realms of space and time, the rock and I.

These quotations from my own early, naive, writing demonstrate, I hope, why I became so hopelessly in thrall to the mountains in my youth.

In 1943 I became a member of the Fell and Rock Climbing Club of the English Lake District, which gave me the use of its climbers' huts scattered across Cumberland. To qualify, one had to have ascended at least twenty peaks, or 'fells', in the District, or else gone up no fewer than twenty rock climbs. I qualified on both counts.

Cambridge University had its own special resource for those of its students who loved, and missed, mountain-climbing. The town is very flat, set as it is in the Fens which are partly below sea-level, but it has splendid buildings replete with statues, drainpipes, stone windows and architraves which provide fine illicit – and therefore nocturnal – climbing. There was even an unofficial guidebook for the nightclimbers, written under a pseudonym by a renowned mountaineer, Geoffrey Winthrop Young. I undertook a number of these climbs, even being arrested on one occasion by a senior member of one college while climbing its statue-studded building overlooking King's Parade. He handed me and my fellow climber over to the police. This was slightly alarming, because it was wartime, I was an 'enemy alien' under permanent night-time curfew, and my place as a student was in danger. That night I spoke with a flawless upper-class English accent, and that saved me.

The Cambridge University Mountaineering Club organised climbing 'meets' in every vacation, which made it possible for beginners like me to learn the various techniques involved in mountaineering and also covered a wide range of British peaks and crags. During my last two years in school I ascended dozens of Lake District fells, mostly as a walker but occasionally as a rock-climber. The CUMC meets took me rock-climbing in North Wales, the Lake District once again, and the Scottish Highlands (Ben Nevis and the Skye Cuillin hills in particular). It was wartime and the rest of the world was out of bounds. My favourite climbing companion in Cambridge was Harry Whitcut, an engineer at Emmanuel College and a man wonderfully skilled on the crags; I recall that he was so extraordinarily flexible that he could put the soles of his feet together behind his neck. I introduced him to a friend of Pat's who also loved the hills and in due course they were married.

For many decades after my graduation, with my wife (and later, my children) whenever feasible, I walked and climbed in Britain, Switzerland, the Pyrenees, the Rockies, the Andes, the Himalayas, Australia and Japan. Many of these snatched expeditions were possible as sidetrips from my many scientific conferences, others were purposive mountain expeditions, once involving both my own and my sister's family. Two major Himalayan treks were done with former Indian research students who made the local arrangements. The most memorable of these many expeditions was, however, my honeymoon with Pat in 1947, which included a crossing of the main chain of the Pyrenees from France into Andorra, during which we shared the contents of our leather wineskin with a group of thirsty refugees from Franco's tyranny whom we met by chance on the French side of the border.

The numerous mountain walks also kindled my enthusiasm for alpine flowers and, in due course, I built a succession of

51

alpine gardens attached to our several houses and stocked them with an increasing variety of alpine plants.

Two episodes from Cambridge days, each pregnant with consequence, are worthy of note. In 1944, a Trinity College friend of mine, Oscar Hahn, a forceful engineer who had been incapacitated by polio and could not walk any distance, asked for my help. It was May, and the college oarsmen had just achieved a multiple victory by 'bumping' several rival boats ahead of them on the river. The victory was celebrated by a pair of oars being lashed, at dead of night, to the glass 'lantern' high above the college dining-hall. There the oars were displayed, to the amazement of all the college. Oscar had a private quarrel with the president of the boat club and he was offended by this brazen celebration, so he asked me, as a known climber, whether I could ascend the roof of the dining-hall the next night and unlash the oars. I told him that I would need an accomplice on whose shoulders I could stand while he sat astride the roof-ridge, so that I could reach the oars. Oscar told me that he did not know any other climbers but he did know a dare-devil young French-Irish mathematician, in his first year in college, who would try anything for an adventure. This was Pierre Young. He readily agreed to join my quixotic enterprise, and the next night we managed to detach one of the oars without mishap, transport it to another part of college, supply it with a pointed message and deposit it in the room of the president of the boat club while he lay asleep. Pierre became my best friend in college. I introduced him to my sister Irene when, after the War, she joined poppa and me in England. She fell deeply under his spell, embarked on a long-term siege of his heart and eventually married him.

The other episode was a little later. One sunny day in 1945, I had just completed a climb with a friend on the east face of Tryfan, a mountain in North Wales, and sat on the summit coiling up the rope, when Pat appeared gracefully with her parents in tow. It emerged that they were on holiday in the area and had been out walking on this perfect day; she saw the summit from below and urged her parents to accompany her up Tryfan by the walker's route – a true mountaineer's reaction. Pat was wearing an immensely becoming pair of brown trousers with a round orange patch behind and a contrasting pale green top. That orange patch somehow brought home to me how much in love with her I had for some time been, without quite admitting it to my cautious self. Her parents were convinced to their dying day that this meeting had been carefully arranged, but they should have known better. Timing in the hills is impossible to predict with any accuracy, and the precision of our meeting could only have been sheer chance. From that day on, I did indeed recognize that Pat was irresistibly appealing, and our relationship developed apace.

Pat and I were married on 9 August 1947, on an idyllic summer day, in a tiny hilltop church above the Warwickshire village of Haselor, between Stratford-upon-Avon and Alcester, in the presence of Pat's parents, brother and sister, and my father and sister. Pat sprang from an Anglican family, and her mother wanted a church wedding. Neither of our fathers was much concerned about how we were conjoined; poppa did not urge a Jewish wedding on me. My mother was unable to attend the wedding, being still in Spain, but she would not have objected either. The headmaster of Maiden Erlegh School had forced me to attend an Anglican church on Sundays for a while but I had resisted this attempted indoctrination and had not learnt the details of Anglican practice, least of all the wedding service – so when the parson addressed me with, 'Do you, Robert, take this woman, Patricia, to be your lawful wedded wife...', I responded with an enthusiastic 'yes', without waiting for all the provisos about better or worse, sickness and health, richer or poorer. The congregation tittered, the parson gazed upon me benevolently and began again, and Pat was clearly gratified. Pat is inclined to blame her mother for not letting her know that in 1947 she was no longer under an obligation to promise to obey me, so she made that promise, and as she sometimes reminds me, she had to develop a whole battery of techniques to sidestep that vow when appropriate. What is more, she points out to me that while she promised to obey me, she never undertook not to argue.

* * *

When Pat and I had known each other for about a year, in 1944, I met her father, Daniel Hanson, for the first time when he came to visit her in Cambridge. I then discovered to my amazement that he was also a metallurgist, indeed a renowned one, head of the department of physical metallurgy at Birmingham University, a fact Pat had never told me. He and I hit it off at once. Another year on, soon after the end of the War, she invited me to stay for a weekend at her home in Haselor. She wanted to see, as she told me much later, how I would look and react in the bosom of her family. The occasion was ideal for me: by pure chance, Pat's elder sister, Mary, had just been demobilised from the Women's Royal Naval Service (the WRENS) and arrived the same afternoon as I did. So everyone's attention was fixed upon Mary and I could sit back quietly and observe the scene. Immediately, I felt entirely at home. Her parents were people after my own heart, and in their different ways both struck me as both wise and friendly, even though I soon began to argue about political matters. I was mildly left-wing at the time; they were not so mildly conservative in outlook, especially her father, a working-class boy who had 'made good'. Her brother Niel was an extremely bright medical student, and while a measure of intellectual rivalry developed I was somewhat in awe of him, not least of his reported prowess as a rock-climber.

Pat had not long before invited another suitor to her home. Her mother, with a slight smile, apparently remarked to her after my own visit that one of her suitors had too little chin, the other too much. I believe that this was her subtle way of indicating a preference.

The contrast, in almost every respect, between Pat's father

and mine, was striking indeed. Daniel Hanson was a notable scientific scholar, researcher and academic innovator, a highly skilled administrator and committee man, and a devoted husband. While he had taught himself water-colour painting as a recreation, he was not really artistic, nor was he musical, and he was a countryman at heart and a keen angler. Above all, he was quintessentially English in a way that I longed to be but never wholly managed to become. So was Hilda, Pat's mother, who was very musical and literary, and a local organiser of the Women's Institute. Hilda was a clergyman's daughter who had become an early student of science at Newnham College, Cambridge, with the help of a scholarship. Daniel had also gone to university, at Liverpool; his father had been a lock-keeper on a canal, and money had been very short indeed, so that Daniel was the only one in a large family to make his way to university, with the help of various scholarships. Hilda had chosen science since she judged that this would maximise her ability to earn, and Daniel as a schoolboy, though a freethinker, sang in the local church choir to earn a few shillings a week for his family. In conclusion, it could be said that Daniel was a cautious, wise man, who reflected before he acted, while my father was a generous, instinctive man, who acted before he reflected.

It is no exaggeration to say that I became deeply attached to Pat's parents. Theirs was the kind of family I had long craved.

Pat's rural home, most of which was of Tudor construction, had been a public house, the Red Lion, in the 16th century. Pat knew that Shakespeare as a very young man had been wooing in the adjacent village of Temple Grafton and she liked to think that he had on occasion visited the Red Lion for a tankard or two of ale. That was an irresistible thought indeed.

When I first met Pat she had not long returned from three unhappy years of exile in Canada. In the summer of 1940, an invasion of England by the Germans was expected daily. Pat was in a boarding-school near the south coast of England.

She was well developed for a fourteen-year-old, and her parents considered her in great personal danger, so when an opportunity suddenly arose for British academics to send their younger children to safety in Canada, they decided – after much hesitation – to accept it for Pat (her two elder siblings were above the age limit). So Pat spent three years in the household of a doctor in Toronto, and attended a moderately good day-school in that city. She felt like a fish out of water both in the country and in her temporary family, and as she had virtually no money even the purchase of stamps for letters home was apt to be a problem. In early 1943, her father urged her to take the entry examination for Newnham College in Cambridge; her teachers scoffed and told her that the education they had been able to give her was quite inadequate for such a lofty venture. Her chance, they averred, was one in a hundred. When she wrote to her father to tell him this, he responded with typical bluntness that if she did not take the examination she would have *nil* chances in a hundred. Because she was so unhappy in her Toronto exile Pat had written much anguished poetry, and that stood her in good stead when she wrote her long essay paper, on the theme, taken from Shelley, 'The mind in creation is like a glowing coal'. Newnham accepted her, and, as she learnt later, that essay was the main reason. On the boat back to England in the summer of 1943, one crewed by Free French sailors, she suddenly, and for the first time in three years, felt much appreciated as a pretty girl. Fortunately, Hitler had withdrawn most of his submarines from the North Atlantic the month before she sailed, so her ship escaped the very real risk of being sunk.

Pat and I shared very similar experiences of drastic displacement in our childhoods and this was one of many things that drew us close together.

In Cambridge, Pat studied intensively to try and catch up with the literature she had missed in Toronto. One day she was attending a lecture on Greek tragedy, delivered by a learned but eccentric don, Sir John Sheppard. On the spur of the moment, she asked him: 'Sir John, what is virtue?' He smiled gently and responded: 'Look in your heart, my dear'. He was quite right in his assessment.

A few months before our wedding, in January 1947, I became a British subject – or, as I have always preferred to think, I became English. My father had preceded me in this privilege by a year. Before our naturalization, both my father and I were stateless, because in 1941 Hitler had deprived all German Jews, whether resident in Germany or escaped abroad, of their German nationality.

Pat and I planned a leisurely honeymoon travelling with a tent and sleeping-bag through France and Spain, by motorcycle and sidecar. Those seven weeks were most generously financed by my father, to the tune of £100 – a journey at £2 per day. I obtained my first British passport, a joint one, and a Spanish visa to go with it, and we set off immediately after the wedding reception. Getting into Spain would prove somewhat tricky, because the French President had some quarrel with General Franco and had closed the Franco-Spanish border to citizens of those two countries. However, it turned out that as British citizens we were able to cross the frontier, waking up the Spanish border guard from his siesta.

Pat had never been to the European Continent before, so for her the journey was a particularly exciting adventure. The motorcycle I had been able to purchase was an ancient single-cylinder machine, with inadequate tyres and inner tubes, but it was quite impossible to find new ones in 1947; the splendid, polished aluminium sidecar for Pat was brand new. The legend 'Just married' inscribed on the sidecar in lipstick by a precocious brat who attended our wedding was annoying at first, but stood us in good stead later. During our trip, I repeatedly had to repair punctures; anyone who has ever had to repair a motor-cycle puncture by the roadside will know what an exhausting and time-consuming task it is. Eventually, in Toulouse, when one of the tyres had become irreparable, I was able to buy new inner tubes by exploiting French goodwill towards an Englishman. This may be hard to imagine today, but so it was. Pat put up with the technical crises and delays with the best of humour, using the time to become an expert on French roadside flora; she also appropriated the various books I had brought along for my own reading. We survived mostly by preparing a succession of picnics, washed down with good French wine. During those weeks we learnt most effectively to adjust to each other's foibles and needs.

We visited Chartres, Paris, Blois and a number of other famous places. France at that time, after five years of German exploitation, was semi-derelict. Nothing had been painted and the empty roads were full of potholes; there were of course no motorways. We had acquired ration books but French butchers and grocers were interested only in money, not in ration coupons. French style and quality in food had recovered after the German occupation and we were able to assemble splendid picnics. We were treated hospitably by various French people and families that we encountered: one country family was blessed with the birth of a child the night we camped in their garden and they treated us generously to drinks, saying we had brought them good fortune. It was a time when the French were really pleased to see English visitors.

When we reached the Pyrenees, we parked our machine near Ax-les-Thermes and set off with our tent across the main chain, bound for Andorra. That crossing took a couple of days. I had with me a large sheath-knife, to protect my new wife from wild bulls – and wilder German prisoners-of-war, who were still, two years after the end of the War, being exploited as land labour by the French, but were left free to roam the local countryside. Fortunately, I never needed to unsheath that knife except for picnics. After exploring Andorra, we took a bus back to France, smuggling some goods for a Frenchwoman who thought that we were less likely to be searched by French customs than she was. We recovered our machine and set off for the village near Barcelona where my mother, her lover and my grandfather lived. By this time, my grandfather was eighty-five and could no longer manage living on his own in a hotel. So, and most untypically for honeymoon couples, we spent a few days of our honeymoon visiting my mother, who had never met Pat and had seen me only once since before the War. As soon as we arrived we found that the plumbing in the villa was out of order, so we took train to Barcelona, bound for the, by now much-needed, public baths; there we were offered the possibility of hiring 'un matrimonio', a room with two adjacent baths. Then I took Pat sauntering in the midst of the vivid street life of that beguiling city.

It was during this visit that my aged grandfather expressed his total mystification as to why Pat had thought fit to study at university.

We stocked up on rice and olive oil, neither obtainable in England at the time, and set off for home, with me casting a longing backward glance at a gleaming Pyreneean glacier. The springs on the sidecar broke, one by one, under the excessive load of goods we had purchased, and we arrived at poppa's London flat with the sidecar supported on a stout piece of Pyrenean oak, a slow puncture and ten shillings in my pocket. The English roads seemed incredibly smooth after our French experience. We had to borrow some money from poppa until the arrival of my first pay packet.

I had a new job at the Atomic Energy Research Establishment, Harwell, south of Oxford, beginning on 1 October 1947. We had nowhere to live at first, so Pat's father towed his holiday caravan to an exposed hillltop site on the Berkshire Downs and we began 'serious' married life for some weeks in this very temporary accommodation, until a frozen water standpipe forced a change. After various unsatisfactory rented rooms, we were finally able to rent an aluminium prefab on the Harwell estate in early 1949 when our firstborn was on the way.

In the summer, just after we had moved into that prefab and our son Martin had been born in May, the devastating news arrived that Pat's brother Niel, with two companions, had fallen off a mountain ridge in the Swiss Alps, near Zermatt – all had been killed. Niel had been married a year before us, and his wife Joan was left with a small son, Paul Daniel. We arranged for her to start work as a nurse at Harwell, while we took Paul into our household. Eventually, Joan married again. Her second husband was a physicist at Harwell, Hans Kronberger, a refugee from Austria, later to become famous in the world of nuclear energy as an expert in isotope separation, and they took Paul back again. Our second son, Andrew, arrived in 1951, just before we left Harwell to move to Birmingham, about which more later. It was hard on our first-born, Martin, that he had to cope with competition for parental attention from both a bouncy younger brother and a slightly older cousin.

Our two daughters, Judith and Alison, arrived in 1955 and 1957, respectively; before Judith, we had a very prematurely born daughter while we were visiting America in 1954 but she died after only two days.

So, by 1957, ten years after our marriage, we were a very well established family indeed, with four surviving children and, by that time, a delightful house and estate deep in the country near Birmingham.

With our family, we celebrated our golden wedding anniversary in 1997, the same year as the Queen and Prince Philip; we have a charming signed greeting from them, as from one long-married couple to another.

Now we are setting our sights on a diamond wedding anniversary in 2007.

6

Research and Teaching*

When, in 1945, I had passed my final undergraduate examinations in metallurgy, Robert Hutton, the Cambridge professor who had mentored me in my undergraduate years, lent me his copy of *Kristallplastizität*, a marvellous book by an Austrian physicist and his German junior – Erich Schmid and Walter Boas – published in Berlin in 1935. The book set out the results of more than a decade of concentrated experimentation on the plastic deformation of metallic single crystals. Ordinary metals are composed of millions of tiny crystals, but using special tricks to turn a wire into one solitary crystal allowed the mechanism of plastic forming to be much more efficiently analysed. There was little theory in Schmid and Boas's book, but since I had already discovered that my scientific talents, such as they were, were not angled towards mathematics, experiment was clearly to be my way forward. Professor Hutton offered to act as a go-between and arranged for me to undertake my doctoral research in the Cavendish Laboratory – the physics department in Cambridge – under the supervision of Egon Orowan, a Hungarian.

Orowan had come to England shortly before the War. He was a secretive man and no-one quite knew, then or later, why he had reached this decision. Although he had been

---

*This chapter of necessity includes slightly technical accounts of scientific investigations. Non-scientific readers may prefer to skim or omit these technical passages.

educated mainly as an engineer, the denizens of the Cavendish made him welcome, at least initially. He was a man who was inclined to become obsessed by particular scientific puzzles and then to pursue their resolution with determination. After my reading of *Kristallplastizität*, the prospect of working with Orowan was irresistible; a few years before, he had supplied one of the crucial theoretical ideas to supplement Schmid and Boas's experimental findings. He had proposed the existence of a defect in the atomic stacking in a crystal, a defect which he termed a 'dislocation', which he argued would explain the enormous mismatch between the calculated and observed strengths of metal crystals, because a crystal furnished with such a defect should be able to change shape very much more easily than a perfect crystal. His proposal, published in 1934, was simultaneous with matching proposals by two other scientists, one also Hungarian, the other British. It is important to emphasise here that in 1945 the concept of a dislocation was still a mere hypothesis; nobody had ever seen one. My task, it eventually turned out, was to prove the existence of dislocations.

So my life in scientific research began in September 1945, as a doctoral candidate in the Cavendish Laboratory, the physics department of Cambridge University, then located in the centre of town, close to the tiny metallurgy department. The self-confidence bordering on arrogance of my supervisor is revealed by his letter at the time to one of his co-inventors, the renowned British mathematician Sir Geoffrey Taylor: Orowan wrote to Taylor that '...unfortunately, your [version of the] theory is all wrong...' He made rather a habit of telling people that they had things entirely wrong, coupled with a tendency to nothing-buttery (i.e. 'so-and-so is nothing but...' etc.). John Nye, who was Orowan's first research student, from 1944 on, wrote in a letter to Orowan's 1995 obituarists that '...he [Orowan] never felt at home in England (or perhaps anywhere). He was always the detached quizzical observer, always the foreigner... College life did not interest him; he would have lunch in the town restaurant at the Corn

Exchange (terrible sandwiches) rather than in college.' He undertook a particularly ingenious and important piece of engineering research – combined theory and experiment – that enabled him to calculate accurately the force and power needed to roll a sheet of steel into a thinner strip; his physicist colleagues thought this was an undignified comedown for a pure physics laboratory, but I as a metallurgist was greatly impressed by it.

In spite of the scientifically productive thirteen years Orowan spent in Cambridge, he became deeply dissatisfied and moved to the Massachusetts Institute of Technology in the other Cambridge, in America in 1950, as a professor of mechanical engineering, and spent the rest of his long life there.

The nature of my doctoral research programme can be briefly outlined. Orowan had been experimenting with cadmium and zinc single crystals deformed in compression and he found that, under certain very special geometrical circumstances, part of the tested crystal collapsed into a 'kink' which was shorter than the original crystal section from which it originated. Such a kinked crystal was very sharply bent locally, and Orowan further found some indications that the bent region attempted to get rid of its extreme strain energy by breaking up into tiny unstrained crystallites. He wanted to understand under what circumstances, and how, this could happen and asked me to investigate. That was the gist of my charge.

In a recent essay, the American philosopher Robert Crease has this to say: 'A ... key maxim that I have often heard scientists mention is: if you really know what you are doing, you should not be doing it. For if you know that much, someone else has probably already done – or is about to do – what you are intending. Your results, in other words, will soon be obsolete.'

Well, I did not really know what I was doing, at first. After some initial, unfocused experiments (typical of beginning doctoral students), I decided to concentrate on single-crystal wires of zinc and bent these plastically under carefully controlled geometrical conditions, and then progressively heated them to give them an opportunity to get rid of their strain energy. I had been soaking myself in another book, by the Dutch metallurgist Willem Burgers, published in Berlin during the War. The book focused on recovery and recrystallization, the two related processes by which a plastically deformed metal, when heated, is restored to its pristine condition and resoftened, and it was clear to me that the process in which Orowan was interested must be a form of recovery or recrystallization. I followed the changes in the bent crystals by using x-ray beams to generate diffracted 'signals' which I photographed. The bent crystals generated very elongated spots, indicative of the curvature of the crystal planes, but when the crystals had been heated the x-ray signal broke up into separate fine, very sharp spots. This had to imply that strain-free, uncurved crystallites had been formed. So now I knew, more or less, what I was doing.

At this point, I exploited my metallurgical education and sought to examine the changes in microstructure of the bent crystals by cross-sectioning the crystals, polishing them, etching them with a variety of chemical solutions and examining them under an optical microscope. This showed me that the bent and heated crystals had broken up into slender, strain-free crystallites separated by straight boundaries which were accurately perpendicular to the glide planes – the crystal planes along which a crystal shears when deformed, as studied by Schmid and Boas – and also to the glide direction.

Poppa once came to see the place where I was starting on my research career and later described his impressions to his London friends. 'He puts a piece of photographic film into an odd sort of camera sitting in front of an x-ray tube, with a bit of bent metal in the way; when the exposure is finished, he develops the film in the darkroom and holds it up to a safelight; it is perfectly featureless except for a few little black spots. Then he looks pleased and exclaims "Aha!" And that's scientific research!'

The meaning of what I had found puzzled me and my

supervisor either did not choose to enlighten me, or could not immediately do so. By this time, I was engaged to be married to the daughter of the professor of metallurgy at Birmingham University, Daniel Hanson, and so I consulted him in 1946. He urged me to put the problem to his junior colleague, Dr Alan Cottrell, and Cottrell quickly resolved the matter. He pointed out that when any crystal is plastically bent, there has to be an excess of positive dislocations over negative ones.* When such a bent crystal is heated, positive and negative dislocations are enabled to wander, meet and destroy each other, but the excess positive ones stay behind. These will seek to reach a geometrical configuration of minimum energy, and Cottrell had recently worked out by rigorous elastic theory that this would be attained when those dislocations formed walls, or boundaries, perpendicular to the glide-planes and glide-direction, just as I had found. When the dislocations arranged themselves thus, the crystal was no longer strained, and the curved crystal planes became, instead, sectors of a polygon. Each array of dislocations separated two adjacent crystallites of slightly different orientations. *My observations only made sense if dislocations existed.* If they did not, there was no way of explaining the specific configuration that I had observed – a form of reductio ad absurdum. So I had at last proved the existence of dislocations; 'polygonization', in fact, constituted the first proof.

The reader may well wonder why this proof was a worthwhile use of my time. By the time I started this research, it had already become probable that dislocations would be at the centre of future study of plastic deformation in metals, and their ability to deform plastically is the principal reason for the central rôle of metals in material civilization. Since my early research, the confidence that resulted from a proof of the reality of this particular kind of crystal defect (and other,

---

*We now know that defective crystals always contain a mix of so-called positive and negative dislocations, which are in a sense mirror images of each other.

slightly later proofs) helped to lead to an enormously expanded range of research, both theoretical and experimental, on dislocations, which in turn resulted in greatly improved understanding of metallic behaviour. Scientists hesitate to undertake research on entities which are only hypothetical!

More recently, it turned out that the silicon single-crystal slices which are used to make electronic microcircuits, the heart of any modern computer, have to be cleared of dislocations before they will function properly. So, sometimes one wants to maximise the number of dislocations in a piece of crystal, and sometimes, to minimise it. Either way, one has to understand them.

Orowan was not an easy adviser to work with, because he paid little attention to his students – though one day, he, the Hungarian, sought to correct my English; the only trouble with that was that he was quite wrong and I was right, so I ignored him. One day he came down the stairs in the Cavendish Laboratory as I was ascending them in the company of my fiancée. His face lit up in admiration and thereafter he was clearly prepared to admit that perhaps I had something, if I could attract such a splendid girl. From that time on, I had a little more of his attention. He clearly did not entirely forget me, because when I visited him in his home in Massachusetts twenty-eight years later, he took one look at me and exclaimed, 'Cahn, you are invariant!'

Orowan presented my results at lectures in Paris, where somewhat related work had been independently done during the War, and elsewhere. I also very briefly presented my work at a conference in Bristol. Then I waited a year for him to offer to write the results up jointly for publication, or to request me to do so, but he did nothing; he rarely published work he did with students, whom he regarded simply as technical assistants to do his bidding. So, finally, faute de mieux, I wrote my results up myself, under my sole name. They were published in 1949 and excited considerable interest around the world.

By the spring of 1947, I had resolved to exploit a little-known regulation: a Cambridge graduate who stays on to do research for a doctorate can leave Cambridge after two years' research and finish his thesis elsewhere, under his own steam, without further supervision. I wished to get married, and for that I needed a proper job. So I applied for a research post at the newly established Atomic Energy Research Establishment, at Harwell, and was soon accepted. My Cambridge grant of £225 per annum was replaced by the princely salary of £419 per annum! My divisional chief at Harwell, Bruce Chalmers, was quite happy for me to finish the work on polygonization, which did not take long, and then I wrote my thesis in the evenings in our little prefabricated house, sitting at a desk I had bought from Chalmers. He had written his own doctoral thesis on that desk, some fifteen years earlier. About twenty-six years later still, our son Martin wrote his own doctoral thesis on the same desk. Pat and I agreed that while I was writing my thesis, I was not expected to help with the washing-up of dishes; rarely have I enjoyed a more persuasive incentive. My doctorate was awarded in 1950, and poppa came to the Senate House in Cambridge to watch the graduation of 'my son, the doctor'.

The man who helped me with a crucial theoretical analysis in 1946 when I was working for my doctorate, Alan Cottrell, has been a good friend and mentor ever since, and I still often, in 2005, ask his counsel on any issues, scientific and otherwise, about which I feel uncertain. He has had a glittering career, becoming a Fellow of the Royal Society of London at the extremely early age of thirty-five, a professor first at Birmingham and later at Cambridge and then Chief Scientific Adviser to the British Prime Minister; he concluded this list of distinctions with a spell as Master of a Cambridge College and the Vice-Chancellorship of Cambridge University. Among his many honours is a knighthood and, recently, the Copley Medal of the Royal Society: this is the Society's highest award and he is the first metallurgist in its long history to have been thus honoured. While still in his thirties, he also spent some years at Harwell Laboratory where he undertook some celebrated metallurgical researches.

My own principal assigned task at Harwell was to study the crystallographic mechanisms that underlie the plastic deformation of metallic uranium, which of course was a metal of intense concern to people who were designing the first British nuclear reactor. In those early days, uranium metal, not its oxide or carbide, was used as fuel. In particular, I was to study the minutiae of a process known as *'deformation twinning'*, a kind of sudden, discontinuous shear of a thin layer of metal when it is stressed, different from the normal process of plastic slip which I outlined earlier. A deformation twin is, in effect, a new crystal mechanically generated by the deformation. This turned out to be a truly fascinating piece of research, full of crystallographic subtleties – probably the most interesting research that I have ever been involved in. At this point, Egon Orowan visited my new father-in-law at his home while Pat and I were also lunching there, and he referred me to an obscure 19th-century publication on twinning in a German mineralogical journal which gave me a much-needed theoretical lead. So he gave me some real help after he had ceased to be my supervisor, and I was always grateful for that.

To perform my task I had to design a novel kind of x-ray camera which allowed me to position a microbeam with great exactness at a particular point on my specimen, and this was constructed in the splendid Harwell workshop. The research was finished in little over two years, by late 1950, and then I wrote it up in a long non-secret Harwell report, which again excited great interest, though among a limited scientific public. I had established a completely new type of twinning – at least it was the first time it had been found in a metal. Four years later, when I paid my first visit to the USA, I was invited to present the work at Yale University in the presence of the eighty-five-year-old Professor Champion Mathewson, a doughty specialist in twinning mechanisms. He, who was notoriously grumpy and had been apt to terrify his students, praised the work to the skies. I felt that I had arrived!

In 1951 my big report had appeared and I was at a loose

end. My first six years of research had imbued me with an overpowering taste for fundamental metallurgical research. At Harwell, I was the sole member of a research group of one, and the director of Harwell, Sir John Cockcroft – who in his youth had been the first man to split an atom by artificial means, and believed in fundamental research – had backed my independence firmly. That was unlikely to last indefinitely, so I began to think in terms of academic research jointly with research students.

This restlessness came about one and a half years after the terrible death of my brother-in-law, Niel, and Pat's father decided to take his wife on a journey of recovery around the world: sightseeing interspersed with scientific interludes. He left the young Professors Cottrell and Raynor in joint charge of his university department in Birmingham while he was away. Cottrell dropped me a hint that a vacancy for a lecturer had just arisen, unexpectedly, and that it would be very appropriate for me to apply for the post, which was effectively in his gift. I did, and was in due course accepted, while my father-in-law was on the other side of the world. That is how I came to leave Harwell, at the age of twenty-seven, for the physical metallurgy department of Birmingham University in the autumn of 1951, at a salary now of a little over £700. Thereafter, the rest of my career was in the university world. In nominal retirement, I am still there, over fifty years later. However, my four years immersed in the new world of atomic energy had various scientific consequences, long after I had left Harwell.

Daniel Hanson was a superb head of department, and I continued full of admiration for him. At Birmingham he had created a quite novel educational structure for metallurgy, especially its more fundamental aspects, and with it a vibrant research culture which had spread the fame of Birmingham across the academic world. The staff at Birmingham, led by Professors Cottrell and Raynor and Doctors Eshelby and Nabarro, replaced the largely descriptive subject-matter such as had been presented to me in Cambridge during the War, by rigorous quantitative treatments of alloy formation, plastic deformation, defect theory and statistical mechanics, supported by books and papers written by these distinguished scholars. The activities of the Department of Physical Metallurgy, of which I was a member, were supplemented by the work of the associated Department of Industrial Metallurgy. In the early 1950s, Birmingham University led the world in creating novel approaches to teaching and research in metallurgy.

Daniel Hanson helped me inconspicuously without seeking to constrain me; indeed, the moment I arrived he provided me with my first research student and left it entirely to me to choose a research assignment for him. Sadly, Daniel Hanson died prematurely of a heart attack in 1953, aged only sixty-one. I have missed him ever since, and have dedicated my latest scientific book to his memory.

Cottrell and Raynor thereafter jointly ruled the department in his stead. Sadly again, Alan Cottrell left for a senior position at Harwell not long after; a major loss to the department.

In Birmingham, of course I had to learn to lecture, which took some time. I also had to learn about students' little tricks: one of my first-year undergraduates, a very bright young man with whom I am still in touch today, managed to convince me that the subject-matter I was presenting was so complicated and obscure that he was afraid of failing his examination. Would I kindly temper the wind to the shorn lamb when setting my questions? He and his fellows passed the examination with flying colours, and the next year my examination questions were somewhat more demanding. Decades later, that clever student reminded me about his early strategy. As time went on, I developed a new form of advanced teaching (new, that is, for budding metallurgists), which involved getting students to write essays commenting on and attempting to criticise published research. That was an effective way of demonstrating that one should not accept everything one reads at face value. I developed that approach further at the University of Sussex, later.

During my eleven years at Birmingham I had numerous

pre-doctoral research students and post-doctoral associates, from several countries, and these years marked my most intense involvement with research. Papers and reviews flowed from my pen, and I took great care, having learnt from Orowan, to include my collaborators' names in our papers and to make sure that they received all the credit due to them, usually by naming them first.

My initial student, Ronald Bell, pursued the study of twinning, focusing on the dynamics (i.e. the stress needed to get the process started), and his excellent work led to a paper in a Royal Society journal. Another student, Alan Williams, from Canada, embarked on a study of twinning in calcite, to examine the nature of so-called elastic twinning. I wrote up my work on twinning in uranium for the first issue of an important new journal, *Acta Metallurgica*,* which appeared in 1953. A subsequent Fulbright fellow from the USA, Charles D. (Chad) Graham, pursued my Cavendish interest in recrystallization – the 'healing' of deformed metals – and that led to many further studies in this domain in subsequent years. Indeed, I maintained my interest in recrystallization for the next half-century. My doctoral research on polygonization, as outlined earlier, focused on the special category of 'recrystallization without any nuclei of new crystallites', and that in turn spurred my interest in the process of such nucleation. In 1950 I had published a theoretical paper on this process, and in 1972 (at Sussex University), my very able collaborator Roger Doherty and I were able to demonstrate how crystal nuclei form in deformed metals, in some considerable detail, by making use of a novel electron-microscopic technique. This was clearly a good choice of topic. Metallurgists are still arguing fiercely about the minutiae of the process and ever more complex experimental techniques are being exploited, but Doherty and I set the whole field alight.

---

*As I write this, in 2003, I have just completed a paper to mark the 50th anniversary of that splendid journal, critically comparing the papers in volumes 1 and 50.

In 1955, my frenetic reading of the research literature, partly stimulated by the exciting new work that was appearing in *Acta Metallurgica*, led me to an entirely new field of research, the mechanical properties of alloys with crystallographic long-range order. This cryptic term simply means that the two kinds of atoms in an alloy of a composition such as iron aluminide (Fe_3Al) are disposed on the crystal lattice in a regular distribution as distinct from a random arrangement. It is a well-established principle in experimental research to try and change only one variable at a time when studying the causes of phenomena such as strength or deformability. Examining alloys in which the degree of perfection of the long-range order can be varied by appropiate heat-treatment from perfect order to total disorder, without changing any other microstructural aspect, offers a way of exploiting that principle. Alloys of the kind I am discussing are known collectively as 'intermetallics'. I also had an ulterior motive in embarking on this field. At that time, the department of physical metallurgy at Birmingham pursued two principal fields of research: the principles of alloy formation (Professor Raynor's field), and the fundamentals of mechanical properties of metals and alloys (Professor Cottrell's field). I reckoned, with undue arrogance, that a programme of study of the mechanical behaviour of a particular class of alloys would serve to tie these semi-detached fields of research closer together. Unfortunately, hardly had I resolved to start my new programme when Alan Cottrell decided to leave Birmingham and move to Harwell. However, by that time I had become fascinated by the scientific possibilities of my new domain and I went ahead, forgetting about my original motivation. Scientists' reasons for embarking on a new line of investigation are endlessly varied, but once a researcher has 'caught the bug', the original motivation is soon forgotten.

Alan Lawley (the clever student who had pulled the wool over my eyes in his first undergraduate year with his claim that my teaching was too difficult) was my first research student to pursue this new range of concerns. When I first saw him, I gave him a list of some fifty papers to read; he came back from the library two weeks later, asking what he should do now. I was irresistibly reminded of Prince Hal's speech in Shakespeare's *Henry IV, Part I*: '...Percy, the Hotspur of the North – he that kills me some six or seven dozen of Scots at a breakfast, washes his hands, and says to his wife, "Fie upon this quiet life! I want work"'. Later on I learnt not to drown a new student in reading, but my initial decision was based on my own experience of what I had lacked when in Lawley's position. Orowan had not given me anything to read, and I had had to locate all my own literature.

Research on intermetallics has kept me happily occupied for nearly half a century now. I set Alan Lawley to pursue a detailed x-ray diffraction study of the ordering process in iron-aluminium alloys, as well as their creep resistance. My late father-in-law would have enjoyed this, since creep had been one of his prime research interests. Creep is the slow but steady – and irreversible – plastic deformation of a solid under a constant stress, and it turned out, as I had surmised, that the same material behaved quite differently according to whether it had an ordered or a random arrangement of atoms on the crystal lattice. Ordering led to a much slower rate of creep at a particular stress and temperature. This study, and other closely related studies, were published in 1959–60, and were among the earliest of my scores of research and review papers in this domain, the result of work I organised in Birmingham, Sussex and Cambridge. My last collaborator, an exceptionally able one, in this field was Rui Yang, a Chinese metallurgist who worked with me in Cambridge, in the 1990s.

Much later, in the 1970s, the creep behaviour of certain very strong ordered intermetallics became a very major field of research, especially in America, because of the intense competition to improve the performance of the creep-resistant alloys used to manufacture jet engines. The hope was, and remains, to exploit strong intermetallics for this purpose. Until now, in spite of all the progress, the central difficulty – the brittleness of most high-strength intermetallics when cold –

73

still obstinately hinders exploitation. It is therefore very pleasing that recently a new family of intermetallics was discovered in America that seems not to suffer from brittleness when cold.

Returning to my Birmingham days, after Lawley had finished his research, I began to be interested in a different kind of atomic order: a statistical form called short-range order as opposed to the long-range order that Lawley had examined experimentally. In particular, I saw that the response of the hot iron-aluminium alloys to a magnetic field (or to an elastic stress) would depend sensitively on the nature of their state of atomic order. To pursue my hunch here, I needed someone well versed in magnetic measurements. I consulted a famous German expert, and he arranged for a German post-doctoral researcher, Hans Birkenbeil, to join me for a while. Meanwhile, my earlier research student, Chad Graham, had himself turned to magnetic research and he wrote a review paper which helped me in my new venture – this sort of thing is apt to happen in the ever-transforming world of scientific research. A little later, another contact, with Arthur Nowick in New York, led to another post-doctoral researcher, Ralph Feder, who worked with me on the electrical resistance of iron-aluminium alloys – work which is still cited today, nearly half a century later. All these different lines of research on a single family of alloys cohered beautifully.

When in 1962 I moved to Bangor, I assigned to my new Indian student, Arunachalam, the task of examining the effect of small unidirectional elastic stresses on the state of order in an alloy of low crystal symmetry, copper-gold (CuAu). He obtained some spectacular results. Although the alloy was different, this research stemmed directly from the work done earlier by Birkenbeil.

The research on elastic twinning in calcite, mentioned above, was stimulated by some research done in the Soviet Union. I read some of this work in the Russian language, slowly, painfully and with a dictionary in hand, after undertaking Russian language lessons from a lady in the Russian department at Birmingham. However, it was not long before I abandoned this study; many of the metallurgical papers of that period in Russian journals that I struggled through were so full of empty bombast and had so little 'meat' that I grudged the time I had spent on the language. I regret this now, for I would like to be able to read the glories of Russian literature in the original! At the age of eighty, I fear I would now find this too difficult a task.

Nowadays, a university teacher/researcher is apt to be assessed largely in terms of how much research money he has succeeded in obtaining from the various grant-giving bodies, and in America he may well be expected to raise part of his own salary from such sources. Things were very different in the 1950s. *For ten years I applied for no research grants at all, not because I was regarded as incapable of research but because I had no need.* I have put this assertion in italics because it will undoubtedly be highly surprising to the scientifically experienced reader. Nevertheless, it is true. Research equipment, before the introduction of electron microscopes, was quite inexpensive; students' stipends were financed either from sources in their own countries or from funds under the control of the head of my department. There was no nonsense about the departmental workshop charging me by the hour for apparatus that they constructed to my design. My first visit to America, in 1954, was financed by my host university in America. On the rare occasions when I wished to attend conferences the department managed to find funds, even in 1962, when I made my first long-range trip, to Japan. My first grant, from the US Air Force, did not materialise until 1960, and then the USAF flew me to America in one of their own planes for the summer of that year to undertake some vacation research in a government laboratory. Like all university people at that time, I was impecunious in my personal life but I did not feel short of resources for my modest research expenses.

In 1956, when I was still only thirty-one, I was offered a full professorial chair in Liverpool University, but turned the offer down, partly because I was worried about inadequate laboratory accommodation, but partly also because my head of department, Geoffrey Raynor, promised me promotion to a chair in Birmingham. However, he was not a particularly skilled academic politician and that chair went to someone else, while I was promoted to an associate professorship.* In 1962 I applied for and secured a full professorship in the University College of North Wales, a chair focused on semiconductor materials. This proved to be a mistake in professional terms and I did not stay there long. The department was indeed wholly focused on semiconductor and insulating 'electronic materials'. I knew this and should have recognized before I took the post that I was not sufficiently interested in this domain to shift all my research in that direction. I did have one capable research student there, the Indian, Arunachalam, who became a lifelong friend and a highly capable and influential scientific administrator and researcher in his native country.

Again I was offered a hint, this time by Professor Willis Jackson who had been involved in appointing me to the Welsh chair, that the brand-new University of Sussex was looking for a dean of applied sciences. Lord Jackson, who was an electrical engineer, was involved in the choice. I visited the campus, was warmly shown around by one of the professors of physics, applied, was interviewed by the Vice-Chancellor (i.e. university president) and, although I did not secure the deanship, a second chair was created especially for me. I became the first professor of materials science in Britain from 1 January 1965. The concept of materials science was new then, but I had learnt much about it while I was in Wales and played an active part in the Materials Science Club of Great Britain, founded in 1963, so the opportunity to put into effect the ideals of the new broadening of concepts from metallurgy to materials science had become quite irresistible to me.

An incidental source of satisfaction was that I was able to

---

* A 'readership' in Britain.

read, upside down, the list of the other candidates to be interviewed by the Vice-Chancellor, and one of those candidates was the man who had been given the chair that had been promised to me in Birmingham nine years earlier!

It fell to me to design the first undergraduate courses in materials science. I use the plural because the university insisted on mixing the disciplines, and the various versions I designed mixed materials science itself with either engineering, or chemistry, or physics, in carefully quantified doses. The students at Sussex were also given tutorials in small groups (the terminology came from Oxford, but the concept was identical to Cambridge supervisions). I still recall clearly giving a group of the first intake of applied science students their first tutorial, before they had heard a single lecture. I fixed them with a basilisk eye and told them that I did not believe in atoms and that I was quite sure that the earth was flat. Would they kindly try to prove me wrong, if they disagreed with me? They entered into the sport with enthusiasm; in those early, harmonious days, the students at the University of Sussex were most congenial.

At Sussex I was so taken up with designing teaching courses and administering my group of colleagues that I had only limited time for supervising research students, and I allocated most of the numerous young people who flocked to us for research from around the world, even before our own first cohort graduated, to work with my young teaching colleagues. The research output of our small group was prodigious over the next seventeen years. However, I did look after a small number of graduate students, and rather more post-doctoral visitors myself, and in addition to my established fields of interest, I now added the brand-new and extremely productive topic of rapidly solidified metals and alloys,* a field of research originated not long before by the great Professor Pol Duwez at the California Institute of Technology. By this extreme treatment, we were able to drive up sharply the forced

---

*'Rapid' here implies cooling at around a million degrees per second.

solubility of one metal in another and thereby to enhance alloy strength greatly. We were also able to produce and study a quite new category of alloys, metallic glasses. In 1978, we organized the third international conference in this new field. By now, it had become essential to raise external funds to pay for our research, and we did that well by the modest standards of those days.

I embarked on the study of rapidly solidified crystalline alloys when the field was barely beginning. Our researches at Sussex University, from 1970 onwards, focused on the formation of anomalous crystal structures which did not exist in slowly frozen alloys (i.e. in equilibrium), and also on the drastic change of phase transformation processes in fast-cooled alloys. One of the researchers who joined me in this endeavour and did distinguished research was Brian Cantor, who later moved on to Oxford University and is now Vice-Chancellor of the University of York. Another was an Indian metallurgist of distinction, Patcha Ramachandrarao, who is now Vice-Chancellor of Banaras Hindu University in Varanasi, India. Perhaps a familiarity with the disorder implicit in rapidly frozen solids confers on able scientists the courage to take on the running of entire universities.

Metallic glasses are quite extraordinary solids – entirely opaque, unlike window glass – made when a molten alloy is cooled at around a million degrees per second so that it has no time to crystallise in a normal manner. A metallic glass is simply a congealed melt. These materials are often very strong and it was eventually discovered that they also had useful magnetic properties which enabled their use in building electrical transformers. At Sussex, we studied in particular the gradual relaxation of their physical and mechanical properties during anneal at moderately high temperatures (not high enough to permit crystallization), and also focused on the practical aspects of very rapid solidification or of glass formation from the vapour. Cantor eventually developed methods of measuring very rapid cooling rates. Research in this field brought me collaborators from China and Japan, as well as from the USA: these collaborations created many further contacts for me in the three countries concerned, and later made possible my attachment to the GE research centre in 1985. During the past few years research, mostly at California Institute of Technology and Tohoku University in Japan, has uncovered a range of alloy compositions which can be turned into metallic glasses at much more modest rates of cooling from the melt. This has allowed thick sections to be made glassy and has thus led to some new uses.

I shall outline later the circumstances that totally changed the nature of Sussex University and led to the disintegration of my group in 1981–82.

I was offered a chair in metallurgy at the University of Paris XI and took it up from 1981, only to experience French academic bureaucracy at its very worst, with very little opportunity to do, or even organize, research. By 1983 I had had quite enough and at the age of fifty-nine I returned to England as a pensioner. Pat and I came to live in Cambridge once again, and soon I negotiated a year in the USA (1985–86) divided equally between a temporary post of visiting research fellow at the General Electric central research laboratory in Schenectady, NY, and a visiting scholar's post at the California Institute of Technology – although by then, sadly, Pol Duwez had died. This year, as well as being exciting in all sorts of ways, was extremely productive in research results and I wrote numerous papers. This reinjected me into the 'anglo-saxon' research community after the two years' desert of working in Paris and on my return to England I was generously invited to become an honorary 'senior associate' in my old department, now renamed 'Department of Materials Science and Metallurgy'. I have been cheerfully attached to that department now for nineteen years and still go to my office there most weekdays. During the first ten years of that period I had two research students and several postdoctoral researchers working with me, and my research on intermetallics continued apace. I even started a new scientific journal devoted to these materials – but that really comes under the later heading of 'editing', of which I have done huge amounts in the past few years. A third of all my 240 publications date to my years of 'retirement', a period when I was blessedly free of the duties of administration. For the past fifteen years the income from this work, together with my pensions, has made possible some enjoyable holidays and occasional modest help to our children.

During these years of nominal retirement I was greatly encouraged by a stream of scientific awards that came my way. In 1991 I was elected a Fellow of the Royal Society of London, one of the most notable honours which can be awarded to a British research scientist. The Royal Society is Britain's 'science academy', founded in 1660. Other academies, in Germany, Spain, China and India, have also recently elected me to membership; a handful of gold and silver medals (awarded for a lifetime's scientific research, writing and editing) now repose in my safe, and a number of other awards also came my way.

I was not the only member of the family who engaged in teaching, nor for that matter in research. My wife Pat was a highly skilled and successful teacher; in fact, I am quite certain that she became a better teacher than I ever was. When we were first married and money was extremely short, in spite of not having a teacher's training, she undertook some teaching in a primary school in Abingdon. She coped, but no more than that; teaching seven-year-olds was not her forte. Then our children arrived, and for the next thirteen years they kept her too busy to think of teaching. In 1962, when we were living in the village of Dodford, south of Birmingham, near the little town of Bromsgrove, and Alison, the youngest of our four, began school at the age of four, Fate intervened. I had persuaded Pat to put her name down as being available for part-time 'supply' teaching when we had arrived in Dodford, five years earlier, but she had entirely forgotten about this. Then, late in 1961, the headmaster of Bromsgrove High School telephoned to say that he was in a crisis: one of his English teachers had been unexpectedly diagnosed with tuberculosis and been instructed to spend at least six months in a sanatorium; there was no time to find a permanent replacement. Could Pat help out? She expostulated that she had no relevant experience, but the headmaster assured her that she needed only to keep the children mildly occupied. So she began to teach at that school for three days a week, and continued with mounting success and enjoyment until we prepared to move away to North Wales in the autumn of 1962. She not only solved the headmaster's crisis, but at the age of thirty-six had found her métier: teaching English language and literature, especially the latter. She taught boys and girls together of the entire age range in that secondary school, and when she left Mr Kyte, the headmaster, gave her a glowing letter of thanks in which he remarked that '...she opened windows for the pupils'.

Once we were in Bangor she met the principal of a teachers' training college there who was on the lookout for a new lecturer in English, and Pat was promptly appointed to a full-time post. The irony was that the girls in that college were destined for primary schools but, in spite of her unease at teaching that age group when she herself had been very young, she did a fine job at preparing those girls and supervising them in their teaching practice in nearby primary schools. She has a superb ability to establish a close personal rapport with the young.

Two years later we moved again, to Sussex. There she secured another teaching post, in a girls' grammar school in Lewes, and taught English there very successfully for some years. However, the post was available only on a fulltime basis, and eventually the pressure of fulltime work became too great. Thereafter she taught part-time in Lewes, variously in a private school and in a technical college, always for an age-group above eleven. She also for several years provided tutorials for first-year students at the University of Sussex, until in the fullness of time we moved on to Paris. There she was persuaded to teach a short, but exceedingly demanding, adult course on English Victorian literature, delivered in French to the Université de la Troisième Age. She was saved from serious mistakes in the language, which even the kindest French are not inclined to forgive, by timely help from her brother-in-law, Pierre.

When we returned to England, she was in time to get involved almost at the very beginning of our country's first University of the Third Age, established in Cambridge under the impetus of a remarkable scholar, Peter Laslett. Both in France and in England, these 'universities' are actually societies for well educated people of retired or near-retired status: the members volunteer to teach courses if they feel able, and all members elect to attend a few of the courses on offer. Pat has taught English literature of the most varied kinds for the past twenty years and has won a devoted and stable following.

Teaching has not been quite the only professional occupation for Pat. One year, while we were living in Sussex, she teamed up with her closest friend, Ann Sants, a professional child psychologist, and the two of them offered to help the professor of education, Boris Ford, who, they had learned, was looking for a pair of graduates to undertake a research task for the new School of Education, which was simply the name for a grouping of local Colleges of Education. Pat and Ann made the perfect team, in the light of their experience, to inspect and comment on the successes and difficulties of the new courses leading to a Bachelor of Education degree, which was then being introduced for the first time in Colleges of Education. They were awarded the chance to undertake this task, which proved demanding but highly enjoyable.

In addition to all this, Pat was nominated as a magistrate for the Brighton bench in 1974. She learnt a great deal about the nether regions of British life as a result of this highly interesting post, a responsibility which came to an end when we left Sussex.

7

The Arts

Pitar Ray had introduced me to Homer and to adventure stories in English. While I was on my own in Workington, I read Tolstoy's *Anna Karenina* and *War and Peace* in German translations, because poppa had brought these from Germany. Earlier, during the Blitz, when I was living in a boarding-house in London, I found by chance a mutilated copy of *Pickwick Papers* and that opened the door to Charles Dickens. For the rest, I knew such things as the novels of P.G. Wodehouse and a few modern writers like Somerset Maugham – my father was greatly attached to *Of Human Bondage* and *Cakes and Ale*. Later, during the numberless occasions that Pat and I walked along the Cambridge Backs, deep in conversation, I learnt much of what I came to know about serious English literature. Pat had been brought up in a village close to Stratford-upon-Avon, and Shakespeare had been her close familiar since quite early childhood. Shakespeare has steadfastly been our favourite dramatist for well over half a century. Later in life, when we could afford it, we steadily began to buy literature – English and sometimes foreign, classical and modern – and critical works, biography, history and all kinds of scientific books, until today we have a collection of thousands of books in our home. I have always preferred to buy books rather than to borrow them; it serves to encourage writers, who always need encouragement. At intervals we have had to sell or give away books in large numbers to create shelf space. Only very rarely have I burnt any books. Two that I consigned to the flames were Sidney and Beatrice Webb's *Soviet Communism: A New Civilization?* – the question mark did not save this unsophisticated apologia from my ire – and a metallurgical two-volume work, by Carpenter and Robertson, entitled simply *Metals*; this was the most unreadable scientific book I ever purchased. Pat accorded similar treatment to a book with the infuriating title, *The Child is Right*.

Pat, who has taught me so much about literature, learnt from me a good deal about music, matters that I had absorbed from my deeply musical father, and as students we were forever attending string quartet recitals in Cambridge. In 1946, I secured front-row seats for Pat, poppa and myself for one of the last public violoncello recitals given by Pablo Casals, in Cambridge – the man and his art both quite unforgettable. He played one of Bach's suites for solo cello, which he had rediscovered and revived with profound success. Soon after this, he stopped playing in public, to protest against Western governments' support, as he saw it, of General Franco's régime in Spain. 'Art film', including the silent cinema, was a genre that we explored together in Cambridge. One day we quarrelled violently about the proper evaluation of a romantic film we had seen together; I have long since forgotten what the disagreement was about or the name of the film, but I recall recognizing that at that point we had learnt to take each other very seriously. The arts have always mattered intensely to both of us.

Music was central to my father's life. As a youth in Germany he had learnt to play the violin, but his career as a practising musician only really took off during the War, after he had been released from his bout of internment in 1940. During that internment he had lived close to a number of brilliant professional string players who were to become famous later, and, having his fiddle with him, he received free lessons from Max Rostal, one of the most renowned violin teachers of his generation. Rostal was one of those who organised a camp orchestra. Rostal persuaded poppa to transfer his affection from the violin to the viola; viola-players were in much shorter supply than violinists and this transfer subsequently helped poppa to build up his musical life in London. During internment, poppa also came to know a number of Rostal's favourite pupils, some of whom later came together to form the Amadeus Quartet. That quartet gave one of its first recitals – a private one – in poppa's apartment a few years later.

An entry in poppa's visitors' book, dated December 1941 and signed by Max Rostal, reads: 'Martin Cahn, meinem lieben Freund zur Erinnerung an interessante gemeinsame Arbeit.' ('To Martin Cahn, my dear friend, in remembrance of interest- ing work together.') One day during school holidays from Workington, when I was in London, probably in 1941, poppa informed me that I had been honoured with an invitation to tea with Rostal's beautiful teenage daughter, Sybil. I was happy to accept: however, it seemed that Sybil had not been asked for her consent and she was as cool as ice. That piece of parental matchmaking did not work out. Sybil later married the German-refugee psychiatrist Hans Eysenck.

From late 1941 onwards, poppa developed the practice of assembling quartets, trios and sometimes quintets, comprising a mixture of professionals and amateurs. That he was able to do this is a tribute to the esteem in which he was held, for it is not at all easy to persuade professional musicians to accept this practice. His visitor's book is filled with the signatures of the players and listeners – famous, less famous and humble – and with the programmes of those memorable musical evenings. One of the amateur violinists was the legendary Tess Simpson, who was the very active secretary of a committee that helped greatly in bringing academic refugees from Germany to Britain before the War, and as an incidental consequence did much to enhance British musical life. Another was Margaret Bullard, the novelist wife of a famous British geophysicist, Teddy Bullard. A further frequent guest who came to listen was Mosco Carner, a music scholar who wrote the definitive biography of Puccini. There were also drawings of the musicians, including a splendid one of my father playing his viola, by visiting artists, especially a cartoonist who signed herself simply 'Victoria'.

His own musical life became essential to poppa's equilibrium. He also took an active interest in professional recitals at the Wigmore Hall – especially the 'new music' of the period – and, until it was bombed to fragments during the Blitz, the Queen's Hall in London. He took me to concerts as well as introducing me to great symphonies and concertos on records. I still vividly remember first hearing Beethoven's Violin Concerto, Boccherini's Cello Concerto and Haydn's Trumpet Concerto; it would be hard for three genial pieces of music to be more different. I grew increasingly attached, like so many scientists and mathematicians, to the compositions of Johann Sebastian Bach. But Mozart, from whom I had received my middle name, became, and has remained, my musical ideal.

Poppa lived up to his ideal of a musical Maecenas, a backer of penniless geniuses. To one young striving violinist he lent his prized Tononi violin for a protracted period; eventually she was able to buy it from him, and he helped others with discreet gifts of money. It is not surprising that poppa was much loved in the flourishing musical community in London; when he died in 1963, the Amadeus Quartet played Schubert at his funeral. After his death, my sister and I endowed a viola prize in his memory at the Guildhall School of Music and Drama in London.

The evening before my first finals examination in Cambridge, in May 1945, I travelled to London to attend one of poppa's evening concerts. He had arranged a performance of Schubert's 'Trout' Quintet, a difficult work for a mixed professional/ amateur group; this was music that I loved dearly and did not want to miss. During the last movement, I looked at my watch and saw that I had less than an hour before the last train of the evening was to depart from Liverpool Street Station. I rushed from the flat, ran to the Underground station and when I reached the platform at Liverpool Street, the train was just beginning to accelerate out of the station. I ran after it and managed to jump on. By this small margin I ensured my honours degree.

My own musical education was patchy in the extreme. As a small boy in Germany I began receiving piano lessons, but they only lasted a few months before my move to a boarding school put an end to this first attempt to make a musician of me. In subsequent years, in Spain, I had no music lessons of any kind. Later, while I was at Maiden Erlegh school, I had a few thoroughly incompetent piano lessons arranged through the school, before I put an end to the charade. Some years later, poppa sent me to an excellent young pianist in London, Boris Ferber, but since I was never in London for long, these lessons petered out too. By this time I was well into my teens and it was too late to make a competent pianist of me. When I was towards the end of my undergraduate period in Cambridge, having for years played the recorder and even organised a recorder consort in Cambridge, I decided to acquire a modern flute and received lessons from a fine flautist; I became quite proficient and could play pieces like the demanding Bach Suite in B minor competently. It was arranged for me to play one of the movements of that suite in the Master's Lodge at Trinity College, for the college music society, in the presence of Trevelyan himself. What I did not know was that playing in a very warm room would cause me to sweat and the flute mouthpiece to slither across my chin and I made a hash of the recital. That experience took a long time to recover from. A thin piece of cork glued to the mouthpiece saved me from that problem on subsequent occasions. Nevertheless, later on, when I was working at Harwell, I played solo flute once more with the Harwell orchestra, conducted by a physicist, Brian Flowers, and this time there was no mishap.

During my time as a graduate student, bored with the flute's limited repertory, I at last succumbed to a long ambition to learn the cello, acquired a mediocre instrument, with an excellent bow provided by my kind father, and had some lessons. In my twenties, it really was too late to acquire any fluency. In later years I acquired better instruments, and further and better lessons; finally, in my fifties, I found both an excellent teacher and a fine 18th-century English cello, but I never reached a standard sufficient to play in a string quartet. Lack of enough time to practice also played its part. Deep regret that I was not able to learn the cello when young, in a steady and undisturbed manner, has remained with me all my life; that was one of the many damages Hitler visited on me. Poppa, in an expansive moment, once assured me that I was '...the most musical of us all', but I was unable to exploit that innate capacity, if indeed it was there.

Poppa had trained my artistic eye by taking me around the London galleries, as I have already recorded. He had an excellent eye himself and haunted the commercial galleries of London, especially Roland, Browse and Delbanco, in Cork Street, in pursuit of paintings to buy. He could not afford to buy work by favourite painters like Sickert, but he found modern work by current artists, notably by the emigré Polish artist Henryk Gotlib, which were within his range. I became enamoured of a wonderful full-length portrait by Gotlib of a young woman, her face turned aside, hanging in poppa's bedroom. He had bought this while visiting the artist in his studio; Gotlib explained that the picture was of his new wife and he was greatly attached to it, but he imperatively had to sell it to get funds for day-to-day life. Not long after my marriage, I begged this picture as a gift and he most generously gave it to me. That gift had a striking echo, many years later. Some time around 1980, when we were living in Lewes, I attended the private view of an exhibition of early drawings by Gotlib which had been discovered, postwar, in an attic in his old Polish home. His widow, who had lent the drawings, was there to open the exhibition. I fell into conversation with her and told her of my painting by her husband. She came home for a drink and a look at this picture. She stood in front of it for a long time without uttering a word, evidently deeply moved. Then she confirmed that the portrait was indeed of her, made just after they were married, at a time when she regularly acted as a model because they were too impoverished for him to hire a professional. She had lost track of that painting, which she remembered very well, and was greatly moved to see it again. I believe that, when I fell in love with that painting, I recognised in it the lineaments of the deepest conjugal love. It still occupies a place of honour in my home.

Eventually, and especially after I inherited parental money in the early 1960s, I became a collector of paintings, pottery and sculpture, and, like my father, took to haunting Roland, Browse and Delbanco. There, I bought a ravishing portrait by the modern English painter, Philip Sutton, of his daughter Saskia, which today has another place of honour in my home. I also acquired a strong affection for oriental rugs, Japanese woodblock prints, including very modern ones, and later, when we spent a year in the USA and visited the south-west at some length, for Navajo and Hopi pots, antique rugs and silver/turquoise jewellery. In due course our children became attached to certain of our paintings and in their turn I passed on many of these. That still leaves plenty of works of art in our home, though now I have almost stopped buying; indeed, there is little wall space left free and the changes in artistic ideals are now so extreme that my collecting urge has almost vanished.

My sister, Irene, was very artistic and herself collected paintings. One day in the early 1980s, when visiting her in her Bristol home, I suddenly realized that we had very similar tastes and, though we had never compared our collecting strategies, we had repeatedly purchased works by the same artists, such as Philip Sutton and Mary Fedden; Irene had also inherited from poppa another painting by Henryk Gotlib which she loved dearly. Likewise, we shared a taste for boldly patterned oriental rugs. It is quite clear to me that genetic endowment can influence artistic preference.

In addition to haunting museums and assembling my personal collection of art, I also acquired some public functions in the domain of graphic art. At the University of Sussex, in the 1960s and 1970s, the Vice-Chancellor put me in charge of the modest university collection of pictures and sculptures, and gave me control of a minuscule annual grant to add to it. Further, I had general oversight, though not detailed control, of art exhibits in the university's Art Centre. In that period, I also organised an 'arts/science' exhibition in the university, following a similar enterprise at the University College of North Wales a few years earlier: this consisted of an assembly of micrographs, diagrams, plots and models that had originally been prepared to fulfil scientific functions but were here chosen purely for their aesthetic appeal. I had seen this kind of exhibition for the first time at the University of Chicago some time in the mid-1950s, organised by Professor Charles S. Barrett who was both a brilliant research metallurgist and a skilled artist. My Sussex version was well received by the faculty.

In the 1970s, my constant exposure to pop art, conceptual art and other aspects of current developments in the university's Arts Centre gradually turned me away from the art of my own time. This burgeoning distaste was enhanced by my years as the university's appointed delegate on the governing body of the Brighton College of Art. My period of office happened to coincide with a total change in the ideals of such colleges. In particular, I observed the consequence of the retirement of the head of the postgraduate department that trained intending art teachers, and his replacement by a go-getting young successor. He abolished all training in specific skills in painting, printmaking, ceramics, etc., and focused all efforts on undirected 'creativity'. The effects were drastic. Although I devoted much time to supporting the College, I was quite unable to exert any restraining influence and I finally stepped down from that governing body. What happened in Brighton was repeated all over the land. Some were delighted; I was not.

This is not the place for an essay on modern art. All that I want to say is that in spite of the fact that I exposed myself to many exhibitions of ultra-modern art and tried hard to acquire a taste for it, I failed utterly. This was not through an inability to appreciate abstract, as opposed to figurative, art;

90

that in itself poses no problems. It was aspects like the ceaseless passion to shock, or the phenomenon of conceptual art where, for instance, words take the place of images, or extreme artists' obsessions such as the desire to create works that rotted before the viewer's eyes so that nobody who bought such works could benefit by their increase in value over time that, by degrees, turned me away from collecting and from continuing to frequent exhibitions of ultra-modern art. The notorious pile of bricks and its descendants are not for me.

Robert Hughes, the art critic, has very recently commented that we all need less fast food and less fast art.

I continue to haunt galleries of classical art, including that of the nineteenth and early twentieth centuries, all over the world, and never miss the chance to explore national and local galleries in unfamiliar towns. What I yearn for is slow art.

I have been an enthusiastic photographer since the age of fourteen. In that year, 1938, I saw my paternal grandparents for the last time. They had been allowed out of Germany, because of their advanced age, to spend a couple of days with poppa and me in the little town of Spa in Belgium, and they presented me with an Agfa folding camera, with an f/7.7 objective and a primitive finder. That camera may not have been of good quality, but I was enchanted to have it and began photographing everything around me: landscapes, interiors, people – of course, at that time in black and white. Poppa, who was himself no mean photographer – especially of architecture – soon saw that I had some talent and arranged for me to receive lessons from Alfred Carlebach, his favourite portrait photographer. I still have many of Carlebach's superbly lit and composed portraits of poppa, Irene and myself, made with a large studio camera: one of these, of myself at the age of about twenty, features on the cover of this book. Before being forced to leave Germany, Carlebach had been a successful lawyer; unable to practice law in Britain, he had turned to his other expertise, photography, and made a successful living in London as a Fellow of the Royal Photographic Society. In

1940, while the Blitz was raging, Carlebach took me to nearby Paddington Station to practice 'atmospheric' shots of smoke and steam. We were intercepted by a policeman who was, understandably, suspicious of what we were doing and only with some difficulty did we escape arrest as likely spies; we had to surrender the film. From Carlebach I learnt darkroom technique as well as picture composition, and ever afterwards I acted as the family photographer as well as being an enthusiast for photography of mountainous scenery and alpine flowers. For the last half-century, I have used mostly Leicas, for their incomparable optical quality. When our first-born arrived in 1949, Pat allowed a passing photographer, who knocked on our front door, to take the first photograph of him, aged a few days. That portrait was so flatly lit and unrevealing of personality that thereafter I took all family portraits myself, usually stalking the subjects and pressing the shutter release when they least expected it.

8

The Experience of America

Two years after my move from Harwell to the university world, at the end of 1953, my family and I embarked on our first journey to the United States of America. A metallurgist, Professor Robert Maddin, invited me to spend a year in his department of mechanical engineering at Johns Hopkins University in Baltimore, Maryland. Initially, one of his junior colleagues, Nengkuan Chen, a Chinese assistant professor, was to exchange places with me, but he encountered visa problems and so, at short notice, Maddin himself moved to Birmingham for that year to do research with Cottrell. As a result, I only met him for a couple of days at the outset of the exchange. The Maddins and we exchanged residences for the year, and I have a vivid memory of Mrs Maddin looking at our modest domestic arrangements and wistfully remarking, 'You will find our house *very* convenient!' When, soon after, we arrived at our temporary house in Baltimore, we found a cake on the dining table, baked and deposited there by a benevolent neighbour – a wonderful surprise and a reassuring introduction to American customs.

I took advice on the best way to prepare ourselves intellectually for the forthcoming experience and acquired two books: *The Growth of the American Republic*, by Samuel Eliot Morison and Henry Steele Commager, and *Democracy in America*, by Alexis de Tocqueville, both of which we absorbed in stages; the week of our Atlantic crossing, in particular, provided an opportunity for preparatory reading. Morison and Commager, two of America's most eminent historians, originally brought out their two-volume history in 1930; the edition we bought was printed in 1953, and it gave us very full information both on pre-independence America and on the evolution of the United States, including the trauma of the Civil War. De Tocqueville's book, originally published in two volumes between 1835 and 1840, is something utterly different. He was a French aristocrat, well-versed in the persistently autocratic mode of government of his homeland, and he came to America in 1831, at the age of only twenty-six, to '...see what a great republic was like'. After extensive travels, he wrote what his most recent American translators (Mansfield and Winthrop, 2000) have firmly described as '...at once the best book ever written on democracy and the best book ever written on America'. They also point out that '...Tocqueville always understands democracy in contrast to aristocracy'. Ever since I first read *Democracy in America* it has enabled me to appreciate the miraculous achievement which is the American Constitution and to understand the strengths and difficulties of the way the institutions of the United States operate, and that reading also gave poignant force to Churchill's wartime dictum that '...democracy is the worst form of government ... except for all the others'.

At Johns Hopkins University my tasks were to offer a course of undergraduate lectures and to undertake some personal research. This last was much helped by the presence on campus of a distinguished crystallographer, Professor José Donnay, with whom I had many illuminating conversations; he introduced me to the use of a novel kind of x-ray diffraction camera which I used to help me solve a small research problem involving twin formation in molybdenum crystals. I also spent a good deal of time writing a review paper on twinned crystals for a new review journal, *Advances in Physics*, at the behest of its famous editor, Nevill Mott; Donnay's encyclopaedic knowledge and the fine mineralogical library at Johns Hopkins greatly eased my task. This paper, when it was done, included a very long bibliography, which had to be arranged

94

alphabetically. In 1954 there were no personal computers to make this task a matter of a few moments, and so I cut out each reference from my typed list as a narrow strip of paper, put all the strips in a salad bowl and then painstakingly arranged them in alphabetic order on the floor, with my wife's devoted assistance, before typing them out all over again. Meanwhile, our small children had to be kept at bay. There can be no doubt that some things in scientific life have changed for the better.

My wife and I also came to know a near neighbour to our temporary home, Professor James Bell, a mechanical engineer, and his wife Perra, who became close family friends. Perra bent Pat's ear at length about the iniquities of 'the peculiar institution', slavery, on which she had done historical research. She was a great supporter of racial integration in the north-south border state of Maryland where we lived. We admired her political activism, but we declined to feel guilt ourselves for the institution of slavery as practised in the United States and the discrimination that remained. By 1954, there were great improvements in the relations between black and white Americans; it is disappointing that progress in equal rights has not been accompanied by the degree of mixing of the two communities that we expected then.

James Bell sought to convert me to the charms of continuum mechanics, his speciality – charms which continued to elude me. The plastic behaviour of metals can be analysed either in terms of the motion and interaction of dislocations inside a crystal, or else the metal can be regarded simply as a structureless lump of continuum matter with particular mechanical properties, which was and is the preferred approach of most mechanical engineers. Our numerous conversations brought home to me how the same set of issues can be perceived in quite different terms and studied in quite different ways, according to one's own professional background.

During our year at Johns Hopkins, I was frequently invited to visit other universities, national and industrial laboratories and to lecture about my researches, and by the time I was through, I had been in at least a third of the States of the Union. Many visits were made in the course of a transcontinental drive we undertook, as a family. These were quite a novel experience – I was too young to have received many such invitations while in Birmingham – and it broadened my scientific experience enormously, as well as filling me with enthusiasm for the openness and friendliness of American scientists. 1954 was a year when American universities were actively recruiting scientists from Europe, from Britain particularly, and I had the intoxicating experience of being offered several tempting academic positions, both that year and soon after our return home.

I did not accept any of these offers, in 1954 or subsequently, for three reasons: Pat's mother had been widowed in 1953 and Pat could not bring herself to leave an ocean between her mother and herself on a permanent basis; her family had always been very close; secondly, Pat suffered badly from asthma (hard to treat in those years, before new drugs became available) which the American climate clearly made worse, and I feared for her life; thirdly, I had struggled hard in my childhood to become thoroughly English, and the prospect of starting all over again as an incipient American was too daunting, for I knew that I could not have settled in that beguiling country without striving to become thoroughly assimilated. For Pat, the notion of converting herself into an American would have been even more disconcerting, after her three years of not fitting into Canada as a schoolgirl during the War. Her new friend, Perra Bell, energetically sought to allay her unease, but admitted defeat one sultry summer's day in Baltimore when the heavens opened and rain suddenly pelted down. Pat ran out of the front door and opened her arms to the benevolent downpour. Seeing this, Perra exclaimed, 'I see that nothing will cure you of your Englishness!'

I had already begun to learn about American characteristics in 1933, when I joined Pitar Ray's school in Majorca, before I had had any experience of England. Now my apprenticeship continued. At first, in spite of all the reassurance generated by the intrinsic unity of the scientific communities of America and England, and the insights derived from my historical reading, I still felt occasionally estranged from aspects of American life. There was a memorable occasion, travelling somewhere in New England, when I chanced upon a voluble Frenchman during an evening in a hotel and had a strong sensation of being, so to speak, at home in a European ambience again. Today, after much further experience, I no longer have such reactions: there has been so much ignorant hostility to all things American in European circles – and especially in France, where later I had personal experience of it – that the sense of community arising from our shared language, overlapping literatures and shared historical past quite overrides any perceived cultural and culinary differences.

Occasional political conflicts between Britain and the United States can cause psychological problems for the British. The most notable of these, in my view, came at the time of the Suez crisis in 1956. In spite of being a Jew, I was opposed to the Suez invasion and even joined a protest march in London, to the indignation of older members of my family. But the arrogant contempt with which John Foster Dulles, the American Secretary of State, addressed the British government at that time was something I took a long time to recover from, and I still shiver every time I land at Dulles International Airport. Problems also arise from the American predisposition to regard Britain as an intensely classbound society. This was undoubtedly true a century ago, a time when American social stratification in terms of wealth was equally intense. Both our societies evolve, and recognition of these evolutions is delayed on both sides of the Atlantic.

I have used the terms 'England' and 'Britain' almost interchangeably, but my own sense of belonging is to England, not to Britain, which is an administrative concept, not a cultural one. Americans are not always clear in their minds that my country is a mix of several nations, of which England is merely by far the most populous. Similarly, the peoples of

Britain often do not recognize the notable variations between the populations of the great regions of the USA, variations which are disguised by the unimportant uniformity of fried chicken restaurants and department stores. Another problem is a tendency by the British to compare plebeian cultural preferences, such as Disneyworld, with high-cultural activities such as the Promenade Concerts in London. One might as well compare the Chicago Symphony Orchestra with football hooligans running riot after a major soccer match in England. Like needs to be matched with like.

Our drive across the United States, via the Middle West, Chicago, across the prairies and over the Rockies, to the Californian coast, was such an unforgettable experience that we repeated it thirty-one years later during a year's visit divided between New York State and California. In 1954, on the way back from California, we made the close acquaintance of several National Parks: Yosemite, Yellowstone and the Tetons. At that time I seized the opportunity of two unexpected clear days – when our small sons had to be briefly deposited in hospital in Jackson, Wyoming, to receive penicillin injections to cure an onslaught of tonsillitis – and climbed the Grand Teton, all 13,700 feet of it, together with a guide. It was the most exciting, as well as the most beautiful, mountain I have ever ascended.

The National Parks are a feature of the great American landscape which we have found irresistible, and on various visits to the country we have renewed our acquaintance with Yosemite (where once we undertook a rock climb), Yellowstone and the Tetons, as well as a range of less familiar ones, like Mesa Verde and Chaco Canyon with their ancient pueblo Indian residues. The more intimate reminders of the past to be found in places like Williamsburg and Monticello have also drawn us back repeatedly.

On the way west during that long transcontinental trip in 1954 we stopped for several days in Chicago to visit the Institute for the Study of Metals, which had been established there soon after the War through the initiative of a great man,

Cyril Stanley Smith. The Institute was a research enterprise, attached to the University of Chicago but not located in any of the academic departments. During its first decade it was home to some of the most remarkable metal researchers in the world: Cyril had attracted such distinguished scientists as the physicist Clarence Zener, the metallurgist Charles Barrett, the crystallographer William Zachariasen, the ceramist Joseph Burke, the physicist T'ing-Sui Kê. Cyril himself, who later became a close friend, was a native Englishman who had studied metallurgy at Birmingham University in the early 1920s, emigrated to New England to study further at MIT and then become an industrial researcher. During the War he had been recruited as the head of metals research at Los Alamos during the crash programme to develop the atomic bomb. His incisive and imaginative approach to research in physical metallurgy appealed greatly to me. Cyril persuaded me to attend a Gordon Research Conference in New Hampshire that July, a wonderful experience. It seems he approved of what he saw and heard from me because next year he called in at Birmingham to offer me a tenured post as an associate professor in his Institute. I was then only thirty. He was considerably offended, unfortunately, when I felt obliged to decline his flattering offer, for reasons I have already rehearsed.*

After this contretemps, it took some years for us to meet again. He left his Institute in Chicago – where a kind of palace revolt against the metallurgical character of the Institute had been mounted by a cabal of physicists and chemists – and returned to his earlier roots at MIT as Institute Professor in the early 1960s, and after that we began to visit each other frequently and became closely attached. From his early years in research, Cyril had become deeply interested in the history of metallurgy, both the technology and the underlying basic understanding of metals. In 1960, while he was still in Chicago, he brought out his definitive book, *A History of Metallography*. This book paid much attention to the aesthetic aspects of

---

*Chicago is even worse for asthmatics than Baltimore!

metallurgical history – the exploitation of a close control of matter in pursuit of artistic achievement – a topic which also interested me intensely. After he left Chicago his attention was fixed on this history, and he wrote a number of further books and many papers. The fact that his wife, Alice Kimball Smith, was herself a distinguished social historian further stimulated his spontaneous historical curiosity, which in fact began in the 1930s while he was still an industrial researcher in Connecticut, where he worked close to Yale University's excellent historical collection. I am sure that it was as a result of our many historical discussions that I was eventually inspired to write my own history of materials science, *The Coming of Materials Science*, which appeared in 2001, some years after Cyril's death. Just recently, I contributed a short biography of Cyril Smith to the monumental new edition of the (British) Dictionary of National Biography.

Cyril taught me about the vital importance of written historical sources in contrast to participants' spoken memories. As the science historian Forman remarked some years ago, 'Though recollection may add vividness and color, it cannot reliably be used except as embellishment of a picture delineated by written sources for the period'. Forman also illustrated the distaste of many professional historians for scientists who dare to involve themselves in the history of science: 'For scientists, history is not the field upon which they wrestle for truth, but principally their field for celebration and self-congratulation'. There is just enough truth in these harsh words for them to make me feel slightly uncomfortable; but Cyril Smith did much to inoculate me against such attitudes.

While Cyril Smith's historical studies often focused on Europe and the Far East – especially on the metallurgy of Japanese samurai swords, which is a marvel – my conversations with him focused my attention on American contributions to my discipline, which have flourished increasingly in the last century. Those contributions have come not only from metallurgy departments and later from materials science ones, but also from physics, chemistry, electronic engineering,

100

mechanical engineering and chemical engineering sources, and especially from the remarkable industrial research laboratories which were an American innovation at the beginning of the 20th century. My own historical studies taught me a great deal about American scientific achievements, and cemented my attachment to the country.

From the foregoing, it will be clear that after 1954, I made numerous further visits to the United States, almost all of them for scientific objectives. I have long ago lost count of the number of such trips, but I estimate that by now they exceed a hundred, some very short, some lasting months. Many were devoted to attendance at scientific conferences; from 1945, I have been a member of the American Institute of Mining and Metallurgical Engineers (now The Minerals, Metals and Materials Society) and have attended many of their big half-yearly meetings. As I write this I have just arranged to attend the 2004 Gordon Research Conference on Physical Metallurgy at Holderness, New Hampshire, the same location to which Cyril Smith had tempted me exactly fifty years earlier. The Gordon Research Conferences are entirely devoted to intense but informal discussions of current research issues; there are no resulting publications and the terms of discussion are kept confidential, so that participants need have no concerns about letting their hair down. From 1976, I became closely involved with the Materials Research Society, a body which had been created three years previously as a professional home for the new breed of materials scientists of whom I had been one of the earliest, and have attended many of their Fall Meetings in Boston, always held the week after Thanksgiving.

Although I never emigrated to the United States, I had spent enough months undertaking research there that when I reached the age of sixty-five I found I had accumulated enough social-security 'brownie points' to receive a modest pension from Uncle Sam. While I have felt entirely at home in England, I have also felt increasingly at ease in America, and can rarely resist offers to make yet another visit.

9

Editing and Writing

One day in early 1958, when I was thirty-three, I received a letter from one Daan Frank, the proprietor of a Dutch publishing house, North-Holland Publishing. He proposed to me that I should assume the editorship of a new scientific periodical, to be called *Journal of Nuclear Materials*, and intended to cover the materials, some but by no means all metallic, which are used for fuels in nuclear reactors, and also the materials used for fuel containers, coolants and moderators.* This novel idea was sufficiently stimulating for me to seek to find out more.

Mr Frank invited me to visit his headquarters in Amsterdam, and took me to dinner in the Hafengebouw, a splendid new building, with a restaurant on its top floor, in the middle of the extensive harbour. He spoke most persuasively about the merits of his idea, and most flatteringly of my suitability for the task. I have never found out who suggested my name, but I suspect that it was Sir John Cockcroft, the Director of Harwell Laboratory. This was my very first experience of publishers' targeted hospitality; since then I have become familiar with a whole personal ragbag of publishers of various kinds and their different approaches to hospitality, including one who tried to get me to pay for a joint lunch!

Mr Frank was not only persuasive, but had an old-world courtesy and charm which I was quite unable to resist, and

---

*The substances that slow down whizzing neutrons without absorbing them.

so I took on this burden, in addition to teaching and research. Later that year, he and I attended the second international conference on the peaceful uses of atomic energy, in Geneva, and there I reached agreement with Paul Lacombe, a fine French research metallurgist of my acquaintance, to be one of my co-editors. Later, I found an experienced American metallurgist/physicist, John Howe, who was willing to become the other co-editor. Now, forty-five years later, I am still involved with Elsevier, the Dutch company that eventually took over North-Holland, and have undertaken a very wide range of editing (and some writing) for North-Holland and Elsevier – but by no means for them alone.

The *Journal of Nuclear Materials* was first published in the spring of 1959, and today is still going strong, having passed its 300th volume. I was chairman of editors for just twenty-five years, during which time there were several changes of co-editors. This enterprise was the venture on which I learnt the skills of editing a scientific periodical, and how to judge – and sometimes solicit – scientific papers, which are the lifeblood of the system of international communication that keeps research alive. *JNM* is an archival journal – its pages are bound and kept on library shelves for decades for reference by later researchers.

Not long after *JNM* started, in 1960, I was approached again, by Daan Frank in the company of a charismatic scientific adviser, the ex-Austrian Paul Rosbaud. The two of them jointly urged me to edit a multi-author, advanced textbook of physical metallurgy, to be published by North-Holland. As I discovered only much later, after his death in 1963, Rosbaud not only had an adventurous and chequered past – he had been an Allied spy in the heart of the German scientific establishment throughout the War – but was also the most effective scientific publisher and publishers' adviser of the postwar decades, who had survived and recovered from the experience of working for Robert Maxwell. On this occasion he was retained by Frank as a consultant. I signed up for this venture too, but the book proved an unexpectedly demanding challenge and it was not published until 1965, under the unsurprising title *Physical Metallurgy*.

Since 1959–60, I have edited a range of scientific periodicals and been editorial adviser for many others; likewise, I have edited freestanding multi-author books and also series of books, some by single authors and others by multiple authors, and am still doing so today. Editing is like smoking or alcohol – one becomes addicted. But unlike those addictions it does no harm to health and it fulfils a vital function in the world of scientific research. Apart from that, editing provides a modest supplementary income, helpful for a struggling family man.

I am sometimes asked: 'What does an editor do?' The unspoken supplementary question is: 'And why is it a worthwhile thing for a well-qualified scientist to do?' An editor performs some or all of the following functions – depending on the particular publication in question: (1) he/she identifies a suitable author, seeks to persuade him to write, and breathes down his neck until the task is done; (2) he judges the quality of a piece of writing, solicited or unsolicited, and decides whether to accept it, with or without emendations; (3) in pursuit of the preceding function, he identifies one or more referees, experts who are asked to report critically on pieces of specialised writing; (4) for some kinds of journal, he identifies and invites authors well qualified to write broad-ranging reviews or overviews of specialised subfields; (5) in the case of a book series, he identifies and exerts his wiles on candidates to be editors of individual multi-author volumes, or else to be authors of books to be entirely written by that author or those authors. There is no school that I know of for scientific editors; as Lady Macbeth's doctor puts it: 'Therein the patient/Must minister to himself'. Some find that, soon, they know by the light of nature how to do it; others never learn. I even know of a former scientific journal that was edited by a retired military man who knew no science; he simply used referees chosen from a list and did exactly what they recommended. For me, that colonel was no editor: an editor must exercise informed judgment.

As I have already asserted, scientific papers are crucial to international, and national, scientific communication, and that is central to the advance of scientific knowledge and understanding. A piece of research is not fully recognized in the commonwealth of science until it has been published in a properly edited and refereed periodical. The respect in which a scientific paper is held, and its influence on researchers, depends partly on the reputation of the journal in which it appears, and that reputation rests in the hands of its editor. Scientific books and overview papers have a different function: first, they have an essential rôle in the education of undergraduate and graduate students; second, if well written, they replace a huge repertory of research papers by a critically selective summary of the information that was published in the best of those papers. Good books and review articles keep the huge accumulation of published knowledge manageable. Scientific editing is not an arid, mechanical occupation, but central to the concerns of what I call the commonwealth of science.

In a publishing house, 'editor' has other connotations too. A 'commissioning editor' sallies forth to find potential authors for books to be published by that house, where there is no external series editor to do that for the house. A 'publishing editor' denotes someone who chases laggard authors, negotiates terms, and sees the book through the stages of publication. In the literary, as distinct from the scientific, world, an 'editor' is someone who befriends a novelist, essayist, critic, biographer or historian, goes through his typescript with close attention, corrects typos and grammatical mistakes and tactfully suggests improvements; he also cheers an author through his depressions. This compendium of vital services is one that scientific authors rarely receive from publishing houses, while some creative writers become intensely adjusted to particular editors and cannot in the long run do without them. Marco Pallis, the author of a favourite book of mine about the Himalayas and their denizens, published in 1939, had the benefit of such an editor. In his preface, Pallis remarks that '...she pointed out about two thousand major and minor blemishes. Her contribution has been such that I look on her now not so much as an adviser, but rather as a collaborator'.

I have sometimes wished that, in my capacity as writer, I had access to such a paragon; but I have never had that privilege. My in-house editors have done a solid enough job: they have checked for typos, standardised the selection of typefaces and located illustrations appropriately. The only notable difference was the activity of the Elsevier editor in Amsterdam, a Dutchman, who did the in-house editing of the fourth edition of *Physical Metallurgy* – all three volumes with nearly 3000 pages in total – in 1995–96. He bombarded me with detailed queries and ensured an almost flawless final product. He informed me that he usually had around a dozen titles on which he worked simultaneously, but while he was busy with my blockbuster he put aside all other projects.

Another creature in the bestiary of the publishing world is the independent literary agent, someone who gives advice on promising subject-matter, offers another shoulder for the author to weep on, and negotiates terms with publishers, including the size of advances on royalties. As any reader of the popular press knows, famous novelists and popular historians can command huge advances, but scientific authors rarely obtain any advances at all, a fact perhaps linked to the circumstance that they rarely secure the services of literary agents, as well as the fact that total sales for most scientific books are modest.

Following my apprenticeship via the *Journal of Nuclear Materials*, my next major opportunity came in late 1964, when I was approached out of the blue by the managing director of a venerable British publishing house, Chapman and Hall, who wished to start the first journal ever to be devoted to the broad discipline of materials science which since its conception in the USA, in 1958, was very gradually replacing the traditional specialities of metallurgy, ceramics, polymer science and fibre-reinforced materials. I was intercepted, literally, on my way from North Wales to Sussex to take up my new chair of materials science there and invited to chair a board of editors of what was to become the *Journal of Materials Science* (*JMS*). This was a most welcome invitation, and the new journal began to appear in 1966. I worked on this side by side with *JNM*. Soon, when asked to define the shadowy concept of materials science, I pointed at *JMS* and told the inquirer that materials science was what he could find in this journal! I worked hard on *JMS* for seven years, jointly with five other editors who between them covered the various subsidiary fields of expertise, one of whom was my first research student of fifteen years earlier, Ronald Bell. In 1973 I was elected Dean of applied sciences at Sussex University and this demanding task so filled my time that I had to give up the *JMS* editorship, though I somehow managed to keep my editorship of *JNM* afloat. Nevertheless, I regard my years devoted to creating *JMS* as my most important single editorial function.

In 1985, while on my post-retirement sabbatical in the USA, I was invited by the young Materials Research Society (MRS) in the USA to be one of the first batch of 'principal editors' of its own archival journal, *Journal of Materials Research*, reporting to an editor-in-chief. With successive reappointments, I performed this function for seven years and thereby helped to launch the new journal. That Society gradually became my favourite professional body and, as I write in 2003, I have just been appointed a member of its Board of Directors. I have been very active as an adviser to the editor of the MRS's house journal, the *MRS Bulletin*, and in 2001 I was a 'volume organizer'; this is a sub-editorial function, and required me to identify broad scientific 'themes' and to find and persuade guest editors who would commission and drive to completion a group of overview papers devoted to each theme, each to appear in one month's issue the following year. These latest editorial activities of mine demonstrate that new editorial structures are forever being developed and improved.

Finally, in 1992, when approached by a bright-eyed commissioning editor, I offered to create a new journal devoted to my favourite types of alloys, the intermetallics – chemical compounds of two or more metals. This journal, *Intermetallics*, was launched by a small London publishing house which was soon taken over by Elsevier, of Amsterdam and Oxford. In addition to myself as chairman, there are editors in America, Germany, Japan and China. In 2003, after ten years, I decided to step down from this quite demanding function, owing to a diminution of energy with advancing age, but my last journal was an invigorating enterprise and continues to flourish under its new editor.

My multi-author book of 1965, *Physical Metallurgy*, proved a great success, and new, revised and enlarged editions appeared in 1970, 1983 and 1996 – the last two edited jointly with my great German friend, Professor Peter Haasen of Göttingen University. This remarkable man, who sadly died in 1993, and who, in spite of his grave illness, continued resolutely in his editing duties until circumstances drove him to his deathbed, deserves some paragraphs to himself.

My first visit to Germany after the War, nineteen years after I had left it as a small boy, was in 1952. My good friend, the physicist Frank Nabarro, wanted to visit physicists in Germany and thought that having along a scientist who knew German well would help things along during what was still at that time an unusual venture. The famous university of Göttingen was our prime destination, and there I was invited – pushed might be a better word – to lecture to the assembled solid-state physicists and metallurgists, including Peter Haasen, a physics research student – about my recently completed Harwell research on the crystallography of twins in uranium. Since the audience knew I was fluent in German, I had to speak in that language, though, illogically, I wished to disguise my German origins. So I adopted a completely fake English accent, but as I warmed to my subject I forgot about the fake accent and, to the mystification of the audience, my voice became more and more Bavarian. At least, that is what Peter told me years later.

Shortly afterwards, Peter was appointed at a remarkably early age to the chair of the department of metal physics in

Göttingen, which he built up in the face of great difficulties to be one of the leading laboratories of its kind in the world. In 1960, I persuaded him to write one of the key chapters in my gestating book, *Physical Metallurgy*. He delivered promptly and became very impatient at the delays which bedevilled that venture; at one point he even upbraided me in Latin! Then, in 1981, he joined me in the editing of the third edition of that same book.

Not very long afterwards, in 1986, he brought me in on a huge venture, by a German publishing house, Verlag Chemie (later rechristened VCH). The plan was to create a whole library of multi-author books, to be collectively entitled *Materials Science and Technology: A Comprehensive Treatment*. Initially, the plan was for this to be a joint venture between Russian and 'Western' experts, with editors from both areas creating books in either Russian or English, which were then to be translated into the other language. This attempt at collaboration proved a total disaster: an elaborate planning meeting was arranged at a German country hotel but, twenty-four hours before we were due to start, the Russian chief editor cabled to say that only one out of four of the Russians would be coming – exit visa trouble, presumably. The managing director of Verlag Chemie threw a memorable rage and vowed that the westerners would undertake the venture by themselves, and so it was. An American, Edward Kramer, a polymer scientist, joined Peter and me; we worked beautifully together, and brought in volume editors and authors from many parts of the world. Over a period of ten years, from 1991 to 2000, twenty volumes were published. Some of these were double volumes, so twenty-five books were produced in all. The Series became a standard reference work the world over and is to be republished as a whole in 2005 in softback.

After the managing director's explosion, the chief Russian ex-editor tried to prise me away from the project and persuade me to join an attempt by the Russians to collaborate with a new group of westerners. I declined. A friend of mine at Imperial College, London, was persuaded, but nothing concrete ever materialised, because the Russians hardly ever responded to letters from the West. The experience showed, very clearly, that proper openness in communication is an absolute precondition of successful international co-operation.

Gradually, as I came to know Peter and his wife Barbara better, I came to realize that he had made it one of his life's objectives to show friendship to Jews, and collaborate with them in as many enterprises as he could. He never spoke about this aim, but it became unmistakable. He was one of the small band of Germans who strove in one way or another to compensate for their country's appalling Nazi record – I know one such Bavarian lady who even converted formally to Judaism. Peter, as I discovered only after his death, did a great deal to help the technical university in Haifa, Israel – the Technion – and on his deathbed he received an honorary doctorate from that institution. It was no doubt relevant to this self-imposed duty of his that he was a devout Christian.

Apart from the German book series, I was series editor for twenty years (1972–92) for the *Cambridge Solid State Science Series* of monographs for Cambridge University Press, subsequently relinquishing this to undertake a similar series for Pergamon, an imprint of Elsevier, under the title *Pergamon Materials Series*; this is very much still in progress. Between those two series I have personally commissioned and edited some twenty-five books to date. Over the last twenty years, I also wrote a number of book chapters for *Physical Metallurgy* and for the big book series, as well as for other people's multi-author books.

A further function which has drawn on my many years of familiarity with the broad reaches of modern materials science has been my editing of technical encyclopedias. This began when, in 1978, I was invited to be a 'section editor' for the field of 'fundamental physical metallurgy' for the first encyclopedia of materials science and engineering, being masterminded for Pergamon Press by Michael Bever of the Massachusetts Institute of Technology. In addition to editing, I also wrote a number of articles myself. Michael's headed notepaper proclaimed that publication was to be in 1981, but the project was so demanding (and Michael's editing so punctilious) that the encyclopedia did not appear until 1986, in eight large volumes. From 1986 to 1991, I was personally charged by the publisher with the duty of editing a number of supplementary volumes, to keep the published information up to date, and this gave me training in locating topics and possible authors in a huge range of subjects. I was also charged with arranging for the generation of a dozen mini-encyclopedia in particular fields, based on the matter in the big encyclopedia, each with its own specialist editor whom I had to appoint and encourage. All this was done for Maxwell's Pergamon Press, which he sold to Elsevier in 1990 under the pressure of financial crisis, before he was found dead in the sea the following year. While I was working for Pergamon in its Maxwellian days I did not know the extent of his offences, though I suspected that everything was not as it should be. On various occasions I was wined and dined at his palatial mansion at the edge of Oxford, though he was so busy with his efforts to become a major press baron that he did not always show up at the dinners to which he had invited guests. His long-suffering and distinctly admirable wife stood in for him. I have always wondered whether my royalty statements bore much relation to the actual sales and monies due to me! In such matters, authors are dependent on the good faith of the publisher, and Maxwell was rather short on good faith.

From 1998 I was involved as one of six editors-in-chief for a new, even more comprehensive, *Encyclopedia of Materials*, which was published by Elsevier in eleven volumes in 2001 – on schedule this time. It was published simultaneously in print and on the Internet, in electronic form. Mine was a highly demanding responsibility, because I had to keep a close, critical eye on the performance of a number of specialist subject editors and to vet the articles which they had commissioned. This encyclopedia is currently being regularly updated in its electronic version, and I am one of those responsible for this process.

In 1985, during my active year in the USA, I resolved to assemble documentation for a book on the prehistory and evolution of materials science, and did so for the next thirteen years, to the tune of some 700 documents. From 1998 to 2000 I was busy writing this substantial book, entitled *The Coming of Materials Science*; it was published in 2001, as a title in the *Pergamon Materials Series*, and has excited much notice and numerous favourable reviews around the world. It has sold well over 1000 copies in two years, which for a science monograph is an exceptional level of sales; for a novel, however, it would be disastrous.

In addition to editing and writing, I have been active in some other, quite distinct publishing activities. In 1967, John Maddox, the editor of *Nature*, the world's leading archival scientific journal, unexpectedly invited me to become that journal's materials science correspondent, on an anonymous basis to begin with. I have no idea who recommended me. I have to explain here that *Nature* differs from other archival journals, firstly by appearing weekly instead of monthly, and secondly by having, besides the back part consisting of short and longer archival papers, a 'front of journal' that is devoted to news, comments, book reviews and a section named 'News and Views' in which, each week, a number of independent commentators write about recently published research in summary form, and express opinions about such work. Some (a majority nowadays) of these pieces, typically about 1000 words in length, give the background to papers that appear in the back half of that week's issue, and are commissioned by the editorial staff; other pieces discuss research that was recently published elsewhere, chosen at the discretion of the columnist. Most of my pieces belonged to the second category and, between 1967 and 2001, I wrote some 100 pieces for 'News and Views', and also a large number of scientific book reviews, for *Nature* and other journals as well. In 1992 I brought out a book, entitled *Artifice and Artefacts*, assembling 100 of my short pieces from *Nature* and other periodicals, covering a very wide range of topics.

'News and Views', in *Nature*, comes under the heading of science popularisation, but of a special kind: whereas most such popularisation (for instance, in journals such as *New Scientist*) is addressed to non-scientists, or at any rate to people who are not professional scientists, 'News and Views' is intended for the normal readers of *Nature*, who are almost all professional scientists who undertake research in a wide range of fields. This kind of high-level popularisation is important at a time when the output of scientific publications is soaring and no-one has any hope of keeping up with all that appears, even in a very narrow range of subject-matter. The feedback I have received over the years shows that the service provided by pieces like the ones I wrote for *Nature* is perceived as helpful by many readers.

Recently, I was invited to be a columnist for a new monthly publication entitled *Materials Today*, published, you will not be surprised to learn, by Elsevier. I wrote twenty-four mostly scientific pieces under the title 'Cahn's Column', until I finally ran out of subject-matter.

Over the years, I have also written a number of overviews of currently active fields of research, for either journals or books. This, again, constitutes a kind of popularisation for fellow-scientists. The first of these overviews, in 1954, was written for *Advances in Physics* by invitation of its editor, Nevill Mott: it was about twinned crystals, and has been regularly cited for almost half a century. I enjoyed that commission enormously. Much later, in 1980, I wrote a review on metallic glasses for *Contemporary Physics*, and received more than 200 requests for reprints. The fact that both of these were written by a materials scientist for physics journals shows how closely the two disciplines are linked.

In the late 1960s, the BBC invited me to join a scientific 'brains trust' on radio. My fellow panelists and I were called upon by the chairman, Gyp Wells, the son of H.G. Wells, to deal, sight unseen, with questions sent in by listeners. It was great fun, but also alarming, and the alcoholic relaxants on offer in the hospitality room were very welcome.

114

Looking back over my years of scientific writing, of everything from full-length scientific papers to short pieces for 'News and Views' and book reviews, I see that I have gradually learnt much about the art of writing in my beloved English tongue. One thing of which I am sure is that to write clearly, reasonably economically, and without too many clichés, one needs to be intimately familiar with a range of distinguished English literature, novels in particular. I found this also helped me to learn the art of approaching a topic obliquely, rather than jumping *in medias res*; that way, one engages the interest of the reader from the beginning. An occasional literary quotation, especially if it is mildly cynical, can also help to lighten the earnestness of a scientific presentation. My last research student, a Chinese, was exceptionally skilled in the correct use of English, and I discovered, not at all to my surprise, that he had read a number of classic English novels when quite young.

When I held forth on that BBC brains trust I was in early middle-age, but when one approaches the age of eighty one becomes a kind of GOM (Grand Old Man), with emphasis on the 'Old', and in that capacity, during the last couple of years, I have written a large number of short articles, by invitation, for a range of journals, expounding my views on contentious issues, both of science and of policy. However, I believe that when eighty actually arrives, as it now has done, one risks converting into a Garrulous Old Man, so I am trying hard to rein in this outpouring of opinion. Perhaps the writing of this memoir will turn out to constitute a natural closure.

Grandfather Emil Cahn (1920s)

Grandmother Selma Cahn (1920s)

Grandparents Hugo and Rosa Heinemann, newly married (1896

Mother and Robert (1926)

Father, Robert and Irene, Palma de Mallorca (1934)

Hugo Heinemann
and Irene (1933)

Pitar Ray, with Martin and Andrew, Baltimore (1954)

Hugo Heinemann's gravestone, Fürth

Robert, photographed by Alfred
Carlebach (1936)

Irene, photographed by
Carlebach (early 1950s)

Irene and Pierre, wedding day
(1953)

Robert and Pat, wedding day
(1947)

Robert, Pat and Martin (1950)

Daniel Hanson - Pat's father, Robert, Pat and Andrew (1951)

Robert's father, photographed by Carlebach (1938)

Pat, in North Wales (1962)

Robert's father, playing the viola in a
string quartet, at home in London (1945)

The Grand Teton, Wyoming (middle summit)

Robert resting on mountain summit (1950s)

Judith and Alison, in Dodford (1960)

University of Sussex (1966)

Far Forest, Maresfield, Sussex (family home, 1965-1971)

10

Sussex University: Crescendo

When it began operation in 1961, the University of Sussex, set in an attractive rural campus between Brighton and Lewes, was a most exciting, indeed beguiling, place. It was the first of the six new British universities called for in the Robbins Report of 1963. In fact, its creation somewhat foreshadowed the Report's published recommendations. The first Vice-Chancellor was John Fulton, later to be knighted and then ennobled: he had taught politics in Oxford, then become principal of University College Swansea, in Wales, and was full of original ideas. The central notion was the need to link studies in distinct fields, and in pursuit of that ideal the University's academic structure was originally based on Schools of Study instead of traditional single-subject departments. Especially in the humanities, literary, historical, philosophical and indeed social aspects were linked by co-operating teachers. I heard this new project described in detail at a lecture given at Bangor, where I was then a professor, in 1963, and was captivated, whereas some of my colleagues muttered contemptuous imprecations about trendy ideas. When I was interviewed for a chair at Sussex in early 1964, Fulton made it very clear that the same principles were to govern the new School of Applied Sciences. Since I was to teach materials science, in its breadth a miniature exemplification of Fulton's central principle, I was clearly perceived as the right man to fit in with the university. I started there on 1 January 1965, as professor of materials science – the first in Britain with that title.

At this point, it will be helpful to explain what *materials science* is and what was new about it in 1965. The concept originated at Northwestern University in the American midwest, in 1957, in an academic metallurgy department, where some of the staff decided that the study of metallurgy was in itself too restrictive, since other categories of materials were becoming increasingly important in industrial applications, side by side with metals and alloys. They also thought that the study of one category of materials was likely to cast light on some properties of another category. Within a few years in the US a number of universities had decided to alter their metallurgy syllabuses and give substantial attention to other categories of materials, such as semiconductors (then just beginning to be important in industry), ceramics and polymers (i.e. plastics). As this was happening in the late 1950s and early 1960s, two other developments ensured that the new academic initiative should not be stillborn.* First, a few industrial research laboratories, spearheaded by the impressive laboratory supported by General Electric in Schenectady, NY, rearranged their research plans along similar, drastically broadened lines. Second, as a reaction to the alarm felt in official American circles when the Russians launched their Sputnik satellite in October 1957, Congress decided to fund the Materials Research Laboratories in a few American universities initially: these purpose-built laboratories improved on the initial academic development of materials science, which emerged entirely from metallurgy, by persuading the solid-state physicists, various kinds of engineers and, to some extent, chemists in their own academic departments to collaborate closely with the ex-metallurgists. In fact, these hitherto hermetically sealed groups were obliged to occupy adjacent offices and laboratories and to undertake joint research. By the end of the 1960s, the new institutions were firmly established.†

---

*This was a real risk, because a number of older, influential academic metallurgists bitterly opposed the new ideas.
†I have described these developments more fully in my book, *The Coming of Materials Science*.

In the British Commonwealth and on the Continent of Europe, the concept of materials science was much slower in maturing. The first development came in Britain, where a Materials Science Club was set up in 1963. This initiative was due to a working party of some thirty individuals, with the objective of reporting on developments in materials, set up by the (British) Institution of Chemical Engineers and chaired by an enthusiast, Dr Leslie Holliday. The working party included – besides professional chemical engineers like Holliday – specialists in metals, polymers, ceramics, concrete, paper and timber (but not yet semiconductors), as well as some who represented user industries. When the working party was about to report to its Council, it was suggested that 'the working party was too enthusiastic a group to be disbanded lightly', and the Materials Science Club was the result. The founding members were largely drawn from the working party, and its first president was Leslie Holliday; I was the second, from 1965.

The Club, which continued actively to the 1980s, held a great variety of meetings at which research on materials was reported and debated, and it published a monthly cyclostyled bulletin. The Club was very similar in concept to the Materials Research Society (MRS) which was founded in America ten years later, but the much larger research population in America meant that the MRS could quickly grow to a viable size and afford professional administrators, whereas the British Club, sustained though it was by numerous unpaid enthusiasts, never advanced beyond about 300 members and eventually was swallowed up by a much larger society and disappeared from view. However, its missionary activities helped to bring about the decision to set up academic materials science departments, of which the one at Sussex University was the first, in 1965. The creation the following year of the new *Journal of Materials Science*, described in the preceding chapter, cemented the new concept and ensured that materials science was not stillborn in Britain, even though there was much conservative opposition, as there had been in America. The main objection raised against the new concept was that it was too broad and diffuse to be properly regarded as a discipline, and much arcane argument developed, some of which continues even today, as to whether materials science is a discipline or an interdisciplinary activity. It is widely agreed that a proper discipline needs to have an intellectual core that is distinct from the core of any neighbouring discipline, and that core, for materials science, is the study of the micro-structure of materials – the kind of structure that is visible with various kinds of microscope, and that is intimately linked with the procedures by which a material is prepared, and with its various properties.

Most of the later departments of materials science were modified metallurgy departments (and the same thing had happened in America); the great strength of the experiment at the University of Sussex was that it was created out of nothing, at a brand new university, and was not weighed down by any pre-existing orthodoxy; there was no special emphasis on metals.

During my first five years or so, everything went swimmingly. The new university attracted large numbers of able applicants for its student places, and (unlike in North Wales) I was also able, without difficulty, to secure promising young colleagues to teach and research alongside me; John Fulton attended the interviews to make sure that I recruited colleagues who would fit into the Sussex ethos. A fine new building was under construction and, under the procedure then in use, a single expert adjudicator from outside vetted and approved my requested list of scientific equipment. The university librarian made generous funds available to assemble a collection of books and archival journals in materials science, which I proposed in great detail. I was free to work out a teaching scheme to combine materials science teaching with lectures and laboratory work in either engineering topics or chemistry. A little later solid-state physics became another alternative. This gave prospective students a choice of three alternative patterns of 'majoring' in materials science. These different patterns were administered in different 'Schools of Study', which suited me well. At the very outset, I set up a series of weekly colloquia by speakers invited from the great world outside, and this continued throughout the seventeen years I was at the university.

Visitors poured in from all parts of the world to see how I was designing the new discipline of materials science. This was the period when my worldwide professional network really took shape. Academically, I was in heaven.

What was particularly pleasing was the excellent relationship between faculty, as the academic staff were collectively called, and students. When I arrived I was supporting a revived Liberal Party in the House of Commons, and I soon found myself the president of the student Liberals. In that capacity I cheerfully socialised with that group of students in the Lanes of nearby Brighton. The small initial intake in the School of Applied Sciences, including my own undergraduates and initial research students – recruited from other, longer-established universities – also had an excellent, relaxed relationship with the faculty. If there were any tensions, I did not detect them.

My first five years at Sussex University were almost cloudless, and this went along with equally flawless domestic circumstances. We had found a beautifully designed, newly built house in the country, north of the university, at the edge of a wild upland called Ashdown Forest; there were plenty of tall trees but the large garden needed to be designed and constructed; we had the necessary means, and Pat and I had great fun with this, with professional help. The children were all doing well and there were no family problems of any note. Our eldest son became a student of biology at Sussex University in 1967 and his impressions helpfully complemented my own. As a family, we formed the habit of making frequent visits to London theatres, seeing the productions of the Royal Shakespeare Company in particular, and we all haunted mountains together, in Britain and elsewhere.

We socialised with numerous faculty at Sussex – scientists

of various stripes, littérateurs, historians, psychologists. Many of our guests were young, idealistic high-flyers who had recently joined the University, and we threw dinner parties and garden parties for them, and were invited in return. Particularly lively parties were offered by the bons viveurs Marcus and Mitzi Cunliffe in their luxurious house in Brighton. He was professor of American studies, with a tremendous scholarly reputation, and had arrived in the university on the same day as I did; she was a notable sculptor. Their marriage, like so many others at that university, went spectacularly wrong later on – there was an epidemic of divorces – but in the 1960s there was no hint of trouble. We also made a number of good friends in the neighbourhood of our home. Tony Dummett and his wife Ursula lived in a manor house in Ashdown Forest. I had benefitted from an undergraduate attachment during the summer vacation in 1944 at the industrial laboratory where he then worked, in Putney, and it was good to renew acquaintance after almost a quarter of a century. Ashdown Forest and the South Downs were irresistible locations for extended walks.

Apart from the construction and maintenance of the materials science group for almost seventeen years, I had a number of other rôles inside and beyond the university, many of them enjoyable. One of the more demanding but highly interesting ones was for the Council of National Academic Awards, a central body in London that was charged with vetting and approving degree courses and Ph.D. programmes at polytechnics – before most of these eventually became autonomous new universities. I was chairman of the materials science committee for several years. During those years I also examined numerous Ph.D. theses at various British universities, and occasionally on the Continent.

For several years I masterminded the university's Open Lectures, delivered by invited speakers from outside, in a manner accessible to all parts of the university, on a wide variety of topics. The originality of Sussex's conception of a university education attracted such renowned scholars as

Professor John Kenneth Galbraith, the American economist and sardonic commentator on current events; Sir Lawrence Bragg, the physicist and discoverer of x-ray diffraction; and Dr Jonathan Miller, the theatre director and physician.

My most rewarding involvement was certainly with the creation and supervision of the Science Policy Research Unit (SPRU), starting soon after I joined the university. This was a body with multiple functions from the outset: (1) to assess, with input from the social sciences and history as well as from scientific knowledge, the case for undertaking science- and technology-based public programmes, such as the building of nuclear power stations or programmes in weapon control; (2) to take a major part in the delivery of the university's 'arts/science' programme – that is, teaching topics in the arts and, especially, social sciences to science students and, more problematically, exposing social science students to scientific ideas (teaching scientific ideas to students of the humanities was a lost cause from the outset); (3) supervising doctoral candidates in the shadowy borderlands of science and social science. The mastermind behind SPRU was its first director, the economist Christopher Freeman, and when from its beginning I was made a member of SPRU's governing committee I came to know and appreciate this remarkable man, who is now respected the world over as an elder statesman in his field. We taught a number of arts/science seminars together and always got on beautifully. When I left the university in 1981, he sent me a letter of good wishes, including these words:

I wanted too to thank you ever so much for all your encouragement and support for SPRU over the last fifteen years. I know you must have felt sometimes at odds with some things in SPRU, as well as in the university more generally, but you were always extraordinarily tolerant and considerate towards me personally as well as the Unit generally. I know you may find it hard to believe it but I do actually hold to the values of liberalism and pluralism almost as strongly as you do (which is saying a good deal) and I have really appreciated your example and your help.

Since I was regarded by some of my more leftwing professorial colleagues on Senate as a reactionary dinosaur, I was intensely moved by this letter.

The respect in which Christopher evidently held me had an unexpected consequence. In 1973, I was invited to be external examiner for the undergraduate course at Manchester University entitled *Liberal Studies in Science* (nicknamed *Science Greats**). Many years later, I discovered that Christopher Freeman had recommended me for this rôle. The Manchester course was the brainchild of a biochemist, Professor Freddie Jevons. The Manchester prospectus for 1973 defines the purpose of this course as follows:

> The Department of Liberal Studies in Science was established in 1966 to provide an undergraduate degree course in science and its social context which develops in its students the attribute of literacy as well as numeracy. There are two distinct undergraduate programmes in the Department – one based on the physical sciences and the other on life sciences. The life sciences programme comes into operation for the first time in 1974. Much of the teaching is done by staff from other Departments but the Department of Liberal Studies in Science takes responsibility for the students and forms their base in the University.

The prospectus goes on to say that

> ... the science components inculcate the precise intellectual

---

*In British universities, examinations for bachelor's courses, master's courses and Ph.D.s all involve input from examiners brought in from other universities, and indeed they have the last word in the the case of disputes concerning the classification of individual students. External examiners have both to approve the examination papers in advance and then to sample the marking of the students' answer papers by the internal examiners.

discipline of numeracy; the 'liberal' component sets science in its social context; this involves extensive reading and marshalling of facts to develop arguments in essays and in seminar discussions.

It underlines the intellectual coherence that binds the subject matter together, and adds that '...much of it is concerned with examining science from the social, economic, historical and philosophical viewpoints'.

I have in front of me as I write the final examination papers for 1973, the first group I dealt with during my three-year appointment. The first paper was a high-level test of students' understanding of physical chemistry. The second, entitled *Projects and Policies*, dealt mainly with energy issues, and in full quantitative detail with issues of planning such matters as a district heating project or the operation of the Organisation of Petroleum Exporting Countries. The third paper, entitled *Origins of Modern Science*, goes into philosophy as well as history of science in depth, kicking off with a question about Karl Popper's criteria for the demarcation of science from non-science, and later delves into the sociology of science as developed by the great American sociologist of science, Robert Merton. If I had, in 1973, already had my later experience of universities in France, I could have given a good answer to a question on the possible impact of the bureaucratisation of science on the creativity of research workers. The more historical topics were taught and examined in earlier years of the course, and the paper on this field was fascinating. It used the literary scholar's trick of giving a number of quotations from sixteen named individuals (such as Aristotle, Copernicus, Kuhn, Popper, etc.) and asking the student to say which quotation was from which scholar, and what each implied.

These papers, and the courses which they examined, were brilliantly constructed and any student who secured high honours in Liberal Studies in Science would be a highly desirable catch for companies or organisations positioned midway between the worlds of science, commerce and sociology. If any such student was ever elected as Member of Parliament in Westminster he would have been invaluable as a member of the House of Commons! Though, in common with many research scientists, I am normally suspicious of the claims of sociology, I was quite happy with its place in that course. Those three years of external examining gave me more pleasure and interest than any other of the many rôles I fulfilled as external examiner over the years.

In 1980, the Nuffield Foundation in London issued a report on 'Science Studies', written by Sir Alec Cairncross, an economist and civil servant of unusually wide experience at a time when the Manchester lead had stimulated analogous courses in several universities. While he judged that '...the movement to broaden the higher education of young students remains full of life and enthusiasm' he also points to the '...limited demand for major courses in science studies', and his report sounded an unmistakable note of caution. Sadly, the Manchester course eventually died, for lack of students, as did a number of other courses. The well-conceived principles of the *Liberal Studies* course came to be replaced by the harsh and un-compromising hostilities between research scientists on the one hand, and a motley band of philosophers and social scientists on the other, that has led to the so-called 'science wars' in recent years. Anyone involved in these wars at university now will be of precious little use to any employer, unlike the *Liberal Studies* graduates whom industry welcomed with open arms. However, things are not hopeless: since 2001, master's programmes called *Professional Science Master* have been established at no fewer than forty-five American universities. The syllabus appears to have a good deal in common with the Manchester programme of the 1960s and 1970s, with rather more emphasis on business skills and rather less on sociology and history. It is said to appeal strongly to people with a bachelor's degree in a science who find that they do not wish to become professional researchers. Clearly, the Liberal Studies philosophy has resurfaced strongly.

The Science Policy Research Unit at Sussex University, still flourishing as I write, has produced many experts who have played rôles in a number of functions in government, industry and commerce, and while I have strong reservations about the characteristic attitude of the Unit to a number of contentious issues, such as the proper scope for nuclear energy, I am nevertheless proud of my involvement, at the fringes, in that organisation.

11

Sussex University: Diminuendo

By the end of the 1960s not everything at Sussex University was sunny. The worst aspect was the 'student revolt' that was begun at the Sorbonne, in Paris, and from there, in late 1968, spread to American universities and then also to those in Germany and Britain. It was a revolt about nothing – in Europe, at least; in America, revolt was clearly linked to detestation of the Vietnam war. The students were rebels without any real cause, but their play-acting ruined the atmosphere at Sussex. I was struck by the response of one of the workers at the Renault car factory in Paris to a gang of students who sought to win Renault for their cause: 'Allez jouer ailleurs!' – '*Go play somewhere else!*'

After a while, a cause was drummed up at Sussex. In 1970, students protested bitterly about the confidentiality of the 'files' held on each student, which started with the forms on the basis of which they had been admitted to the university. That issue was soon resolved, only to be replaced by other factitious issues including, indeed, the American war in Vietnam – the faculty were instructed to get the war stopped, an issue in which British universities did not exactly have much influence. It did not help at all when British government ministers who had been invited to speak on campus, and visiting American 'high-ups', were yelled down by mobs of student toughs. Even the new Vice-Chancellor who had succeeded Lord Fulton, Asa Briggs, a man who was notably tolerant of students' absurdities, was shouted down when he gave an academic lecture on the centenary of the British Education Act of 1870; he was not so tolerant about that. The growing resistance of successive British governments to the financial demands of universities began at this time. But the worst consequence was the destruction of the affable relations between students and faculty: it became the orthodoxy that no student society should have any formal involvement with faculty, and suspicion and hostility became the rule. The student revolt continued, at various levels of severity, well into the 1970s.

It is striking that, whereas at Sussex University the effect of the student revolt was to turn students against the faculty, at Harvard, according to a recently published memoir by Harvard Professor Richard Pipes, the effect was the opposite. There, he asserted, professors had dwelt in splendid seclusion until the student rebels invaded their privacy, and thereafter they became more accessible to the student body. In Sussex, at least, there were no threats with firearms as there were on some American campuses.

Even the engineers in the School of Applied Sciences at Sussex were infected, although elsewhere professional disciplines like engineering, architecture, medicine and the law were relatively immune to the new madness. A severely maladjusted young man whipped up rebelliousness about examination schedules and one day, in 1973 if I remember right, I witnessed an onslaught by a mob of engineering students on the locked entrance doors of the Applied Sciences building, while, as it chanced, a group of headmasters who had been invited to tour the university also looked on from a nearby vantage point. Applications to come to Sussex fell sharply after this. My own graduate numbers, in materials science, peaked in 1976 at seventeen B.Sc.s (the 1973 intake) and then declined sharply. It is true that, from about this time onwards, applications to study hard sciences at all British universities began to decline, just as they have done elsewhere in the West. But at Sussex, the decline was sudden and sharp.

One of the targets of the rebels ('revellers' would have been a more accurate term) was the supposed villainy of the companies that supported research in applied sciences. Here is a paragraph from a letter I wrote in late 1975, in my capacity as dean, to the Sussex student newspaper:

One of my colleagues, Dr Roger Doherty, is abroad on leave, so I do think that I should put in a word on his behalf. Indeed, Alcan (a delightful firm which makes the raw material for saucepans and aeroplanes) supports him in his research on stir-casting. As is generally the case in the School, Dr Doherty decided what he wanted to do and then found a sponsor for it. The £2,400 has all been spent on a maintenance grant for a very capable graduate student, married with children, who is a refugee from the tyrannical régime in Chile. Does that, I wonder, cleanse the filthy lucre?

A little later, I received a letter from an Argentine physicist friend, to whom I had taught crystallography years before during one of my visits to his country. 1976 was the period of the 'dirty war' in Argentina, when a military dictator ordered the kidnapping, torture and then disappearance of numerous opponents of the dictatorship. This physicist's teenage son was tempted to challenge the régime and he was terrified that his son would soon disappear. Could I arrange a research post for him at Sussex and get his son accepted as an undergraduate? Fortunately, the Science Policy Research Unit was able to take on the father and the university agreed, at very short notice, to accept the boy to study social science; financial support was also arranged. Father, mother and son arrived, and the son at once plunged head first into the current student rebellion, protesting publicly and violently about supposed wrongs which he could not have observed, having only just arrived. Many young people behaved out of normal character, partly, I suppose, because of young people's passion not to be out of step with their contemporaries.

Research in my group continued at a high level throughout

my time at Sussex, and its reputation both within the School of Applied Sciences and in the world outside was riding high. The visibly excellent personal relationships which I had succeeded in maintaining within my small group, in the face of all the harshness and suspicion elsewhere, were no doubt the reason for my election as second dean of the School in the summer of 1973. Thus began an extremely hard-working five years of deanship, increasingly dominated by the endless series of financial crises which were the clear result of the government's reaction to the student excesses all over the nation. A British dean has much less authority than his American counterpart, and so I had few weapons with which to fight my corner of the perpetual wars over resources, posts and space. Nevertheless, when the end of my term came in 1978, I was approached by colleagues (of several constituent disciplines) who begged me to stand again, assuring me that I would be elected; but I was physically and emotionally at the end of my tether and declined. The election of a mechanical engineer as the third dean, as it turned out, spelled the doom of the materials science group in the School, as the senior engineers seized all the resources going. The sharp drop in student numbers provided the excuse for the butchery by the School of Engineering (as the School of Applied Sciences had been rechristened) of my excellent group, a process which was completed by 1981. The seventy doctorates in my discipline – a large fraction of all the doctorates awarded in the entire School – were not enough to save the group.

As a coda to this pair of chapters, with their record of the best of times and the worst of times, I feel impelled to quote a few lines from a few of the numerous farewell letters I received when I negotiated a chair of metallurgy in Paris and left Sussex in the summer of 1981. My motive is not vainglory but rather self-defence: as I have indicated, I was regarded by some of my more radical colleagues on the University Senate – of whom there were many – as a hopeless reactionary. Others saw me a little differently.

One of my senior materials science colleagues, Bryan Harris, who had left some time before to take up a chair at the University of Bath, wrote:

All of us who have participated in any way in the work of the Materials Science group at Sussex know very well what we owe you for the good days, the opportunities in teaching and research, and the freedom to grow, each in our own way, and no matter what the future holds, we can be proud of what we created under your leadership. I honestly do not think that we shall see the like of those golden Sussex days of the late 1960s in the UK university system again.

Twenty years later, Bryan was treated at the University of Bath in much the same way as I had been in 1981, his prophecy all too justified.

One of the lecturers in mechanical engineering at Sussex, John Richardson, wrote:

...to express my appreciation of everything you have done for the university in general and the School in particular... I came to respect you for your integrity and your immense capacity for work... When I came to Sussex in 1971, there seemed to be several divisions and factions within the School... During your deanship, though, the School became more cohesive and a happier place in which to work.

A historian friend, Professor Geoffrey Best, who left Sussex at the same time as I did, wrote:

You say that you loved Sussex very much at one time. So did I. So obviously have done many people who have learnt, alas, to unlove some aspects of it with equal intensity. The damnable and tragic thing about the place is that so much of it is very good: original, caring, clever, enterprising ... [but] has it not some fatal disease in its veins?

Fortunately, one thing cannot be taken away, and that is the scientific and social record of my little group and its many undergraduate (189) and doctoral (70) students and post-graduate research fellows (55) over the years. One of them has even recently become a vice-chancellor of a major British university, a more effective one, I believe, than most of those who followed Lord Fulton at Sussex in rather rapid succession. I was comforted recently, during a conference at a university in Rome, to read on a wall, in very large letters, a quotation from Leonardo da Vinci: 'Tristo è quel discipolo che non avanza il suo maestro' ... that is to say, 'A disciple who does not overtake his teacher is a sad creature indeed'. In the group, we were blessed with many disciples who in due course came to overtake us.

I left Sussex University in the autumn of 1981, bound for an academic post in France. Since then, I have kept in touch with Sussex, that place for which, over so many years, I had cared intensely. The fact that the Senate made me an emeritus professor after my departure made it easier for me to keep a finger on its pulse. It is a sad fact that the principal feature which distinguished Sussex University from other British universities when it was first set up, progressively disappeared. This was the linking of disciplines in the teaching programme through the creation of Schools of Studies: a major topic would be complemented by alternative 'contextual courses', as for instance materials science, as a major, complemented by carefully selected courses in inorganic and physical chemistry, or solid-state physics, or mechanical and electronic engineering. In certain fields, of which psychology was a notable example, this form of programme design led to world-famous degrees.

The problem was, I believe, that when the university was first set up and 'sold' to the schoolboys and girls of Britain, and overseas too, it became intensely fashionable. The 1960s were, in any case, a period when fashion ruled supreme in Britain, and Sussex University quickly became a kind of accompaniment to Carnaby Street and the Beatles. This fashionable appeal was supplemented by the magnificent architecture of the early university buildings, designed by Sir Basil Spence, which I still recall with nostalgia.

It could not last. After about 1973, when the government largesse which had made that university possible was replaced by ever-increasing caution in the national Treasury, and at the same time the much publicised misdemeanours of student toughs apparently discouraged some schools from recommending the university to their pupils, Sussex University ceased to be fashionable and crescendo was replaced by diminuendo. One distressing paradox was that although the science faculty was extremely distinguished and productive, and included several Nobel prize-winners and numerous fellows of the Royal Society, the intake of undergraduates wishing to study chemistry, physics, mathematics, astronomy and even biology (which held up longer than the other disciplines) progressively fell to levels which induced the university authorities to merge physics, astronomy, mathematics, 'informatics' and all aspects of engineering into a single unwieldy 'School of Science and Technology'. Chemistry and integrated biology have been combined into another big School, 'Life Sciences'. The structure of the university is now a pale shadow of what was created so hopefully in 1961. The one impressive innovation is the Medical School which has recently begun operation, and shows every sign of being fashionable. The wheel turns.

12

The World Restored

Here I shall record something of my parents' lives once the War was at length over, completing the story begun earlier. Poppa stayed in Britain till his death in 1963, but as soon as travelling to Germany became possible, in 1946, he did revisit Fürth, Nürnberg and München, haunts of his youth. He ordered a made-to-measure suit from his old tailor in Nürnberg, and was delighted to be recognised sympathetically. He also revisited a pre-Nazi flame in München.

For poppa, relations with women were always bedevilled by the profound conviction that the grass on the other side of the mountain is greener, and indeed often he found it to be of a most vivid colour. He owned a favourite picture which now hangs in my house, a handsome etching of a baroque Italian painting showing a woman singer ardently accompanied by a young male violinist, a very young girl with a guitar peering flirtatiously over the singer's shoulder. Underneath the image is a piece of Italian verse: 'L'uomo è discorde, e l'armonia gli piace; E cercando il piacer non ha mai pace' ... that is, 'Man is discord, and harmony pleases him; and in seeking pleasure he foregoes his peace.'

Poppa made one more attempt at marriage, in 1953, to Rosemary, a close friend of Pat's family, a lady of mixed Czech/English parentage, whom he had met at our wedding. That marriage did not last long; by this time, it turned out that poppa could not endure to share his cherished apartment both day and night with anyone else, and his new wife's attempts to 'reform' him were fatal. Some time after that catastrophic second attempt, he found Anne, another young lady, of Austrian birth, living in London, with whom he settled into a harmonious semi-detached cohabitation which lasted until his death. During those final years, plainly his active musical life helped to keep him on an even keel. Pat and I have also enjoyed a harmonious relationship with Anne which endures to this day.

Poppa's business, Cahn and Bendit Ltd., prospered until he died. There was a difficult stage when he resolved to buy out his Swiss partner, whose abilities he did not respect. Finding the money for this was a serious problem. It seems that he tried to obtain a long-term loan from his cousin Max Sondheimer, who also lived in London, but his appeal was turned down, to his indignation. In the end he used some of the money paid out to himself – and to him on behalf of Irene and myself – from the German post-war restitution scheme ('Wiedergutmachung'). He never explained this to us during his lifetime and Irene, in particular, became very upset about the apparent disappearance of her money, and suspected me of theft. This alarming misunderstanding was not cleared up until after my father's death, but in the long run these funds returned to Irene and me through the proceeds of the sale of his firm, which by then was in his sole name.

Poppa was always at heart a 'Continental'; nevertheless, he adjusted well to life as an adoptive Englishman. He and my wife were both justifiably proud of the fact that, different as they were from each other, they progressively adapted to each other; poppa saw that I was fortunate to have such a loving and intelligent wife and that he in turn was fortunate in his grandchildren. I never forgot his visit to Pat in hospital just after the arrival of our firstborn, named Martin in honour of poppa. He came laden with a splendid housecoat for her at a time of stringent clothes-rationing – we did not enquire where the coupons had come from and, fortunately, Pat regained her figure rapidly, so that the housecoat fitted spectacularly. Pat came to recognize poppa's warmth, generosity and devotion to his family. He visited us in our successive homes till the end of his life. While we did not go on vacation with him – he would have found the four small children too much to cope with – we often stayed with him in London. On one such occasion, Alison, aged three, wandered off, unnoticed, into the maelstrom of London traffic and was delivered back to us by a bemused policeman; she was always hyper-adventurous. I accompanied poppa on visits to his beloved piece of woodland on the outskirts of London, and there helped him to gather and chop firewood; he had kept something of the romantic German attachment to forests. His favourite sister, Stefanie, often crossed the Atlantic and called in at the London flat. She was with him in London during his final illness.

My mother, grandfather and Carlos remained cautiously in Spain until the summer of 1948. In June of that year, the old German currency was reformed, the unstable Reichsmark being replaced by the new Deutschemark, and the German 'Wirtschaftswunder', the economic miracle, promptly took off. My grandfather, although by now aged eighty-six, kept a close eye on events and realized that the time had come for the family to return to Fürth, reclaim its property and campaign for restitution for persecution suffered and for the huge 'flight tax' paid in 1933. In August 1948, Pat and I voyaged on our motorcycle and sidecar to Switzerland for a first-anniversary alpine holiday, and there met and dined with the family in a hotel in Bern, as they were on the way back to Germany, fifteen years almost to the day after having escaped. My grandfather took formal possession once again of his company, which was now operated by Dr Dietl, the widower of my grandfather's loyal longtime chief secretary. The family was unable to return to the suburban villa, because that was now a private clinic, but ownership of it was restored to my grandfather and mother. Carlos was able to help his relatives who had remained in Germany and become impoverished.

So, the family fell on its feet and was not in financial difficulties when they returned to Germany. They were in a very small minority: few German (or Austrian) Jewish survivors returned. They simply could not face the prospect. Even some of those who did return were not sufficiently at ease to stay in the long run, and today the Jewish population of Germany consists largely of Russian Jewish refugees from Soviet tyranny, many of them agnostic – an irony indeed.

My grandfather died just before his 88th birthday at the end of 1949 and was buried in the Jewish cemetery in Fürth, one of the few postwar graves in a sea of prewar burials. The old Jewish cemetery in Fürth had been desecrated and entirely destroyed by local Nazis, but the newer one was left alone, possibly because it contained so many graves of Jews who had died for Germany in the 1870 and 1914 wars. My mother continued to live in Fürth with Carlos, until he died in 1954, and thereafter quite alone; she did not want to live in England. Irene and I saw her at intervals; on one occasion I took our three-year-old son Martin to visit her in Fürth in 1952 (she had not met him until then), and there I also revisited locations from my childhood, such as the stone lion in the town park into whose mouth I had used to stuff ivy leaves to save him from starvation; now Martin did the feeding. Mother also visited my family occasionally in Birmingham and, from 1957, at our country home nearby.

Mother died in 1962. Irene and I flew over for the funeral; she was buried close to her father, the tyrant who would not have her educated and lifesaver who had saved her from deportation to the gas-chambers of Auschwitz. We then discovered from the accounts we were given that Dr Dietl, who was still running Heinemann and Schwarzmann, the glass firm, and had handled the finances of the family's villa also, had systematically cheated mother in the payments he had forwarded to her. When this became unambiguously clear, Irene and I had the building and the firm sold over Dietl's head, and a little later, the villa also. If we had waited ten years or so, we would certainly have netted much more as Germany became more prosperous, but we could not bear the idea of owning possessions in Germany in the long run.

140

Apart from one scientific expedition to Würzburg in 1984, when I made a sidetrip to show my old haunts to Pat, I did not visit Fürth again until 2002, when I paid respects to my ancestors' graves, including that of my beloved Philitante whose grave was entirely obscured by trees, which I had to hack away, and had clearly not been visited for almost seventy years. I no longer felt anything for the place where my first years had been spent.

During the 2002 visit I saw that the old family villa of 1930, although officially regarded as an architectural heirloom, had been unceremoniously demolished to make room for a group of smaller but more profitable residences. However, grandfather's office building in the Jugendstil, a hundred years old, is still there, as handsome as ever.

Irene married her beloved Pierre Young in 1953, and they lived the rest of their lives – in due course with their two children, Michèle and Thomas – in Bristol, where Pierre became an engineer in an aero-engine firm which was later taken over by Rolls-Royce. There he became a very senior and highly respected figure; for some years he masterminded the British end of the design for the Anglo-French Olympus engines for the supersonic Concorde aircraft, and for a while he was seconded to Derby to be chief engineer of Rolls-Royce there. But Irene refused to follow him there, so he came back to Bristol. After her extremely disturbed childhood, stability in her surroundings had become indispensable to her. Although she was a skilled linguist and trained interpreter, after her marriage she never worked professionally again. Pierre was bilingual in English and French; when he was working on the Concorde engines, one day the interpreter failed to turn up for an engineers' discussion, and he was invited to substitute for her. The first speaker who discoursed at considerable length, was a French engineer; he talked and talked, and Pierre said nothing. At length the chairman intervened and asked whether Pierre would summarise what had been said. Pierre responded that he would do so, just as soon as his French opposite number had said something.

141

We visited each other frequently. Some of these visits were combined with scientific expeditions to the Physics Department at the University of Bristol, where I had connections. Pierre had been my best friend at Cambridge and remained my closest friend, apart from my wife, for the rest of his life. He died relatively young in 1985, at the age of fifty-nine, from the consequences of stomach cancer, and Irene followed him, succumbing to lung cancer in 1990.

Pierre was a remarkable man indeed. As an undergraduate he had not taken his mathematical studies seriously, mistakenly thinking that he already knew enough to get a good degree; when years later he was elected to fellowship of the Royal Society, Trinity College was amazed at this unforeseen mark of high distinction. He loved a good intellectual argument, irrespective of the subject: science, politics, philosophy, literature, all were good for an energetic dispute, and he always argued to win, using every rhetorical trick at his disposal. Pat in particular loved these contests during our numerous visits to Bristol. Pierre built up a close friendship with Stefan Körner, professor of philosophy at Bristol University, and his forceful wife Edith, centred on philosophical and political arguments. Towards the end of his life he had something of a falling-out with his superiors at Rolls-Royce, and the award, not long before his death, of the gold medal of the Royal Aeronautical Society was a reassurance to him of his distinction as an engineer. He treasured a letter of warm admiration from Sir Frank Whittle, the British inventor of the jet engine, received on his election to Fellowship of the Royal Society in 1974. Pierre and Irene left two children and two grandchildren.

Pat and I have twelve grandchildren via our four children. The long-term survival of our genes seems assured.

13

Science as a Motive for Travel

Attending scientific conferences is an occupational hazard for all research scientists. Researchers exchange findings there in the shape of formal presentations, usually in English – or an approximation thereto. As I became older and better known, I was often invited and had my expenses taken care of. I have long since lost count of the number of such meetings I have attended around the world. They certainly run to well over a hundred in about thirty-six countries. Often we have managed to combine such visits with a short holiday. Sometimes the organizers, seeking to persuade as many scientists as possible to come, choose beauty spots as locations, and that makes a combined scientific jamboree and marital holiday particularly worthwhile. It does not always work out well, however. Not long ago, I took my wife with me to Hawaii for a conference, and en route visited the Volcanoes National Park, where she inhaled some lungfuls of sulphur dioxide-laden air and nearly died.

Many conferences are organised by the huge array of professional societies, others again by commercial bodies run for profit, while a select few are run by self-perpetuating oligarchies. Thus, in 1970 I attended a symposium in Yugoslavia, organised by the local physics society and devoted to metals and alloys rapidly quenched from the molten state (an 'RQ' symposium). An organising committee was elected at the conference and this committee decided on the place and time of the next conference, five years later, and who was to run that. It was in fact held in Cambridge, Massachusetts, and organised by some MIT professors. Thereafter, there has been a symposium on rapid quenching – RQ – every three years. I organised the third, at the University of Sussex, in 1978. The 12th RQ Symposium has been convened in Korea in the summer of 2005 and I have been invited to present a historical overview of the field – but illness has stymied this.

A critically evaluated subset of the papers presented at each symposium is published, usually in an archival scientific journal chosen by the current organising committee. As I know very well from personal experience, organising such a meeting is a very demanding challenge indeed: it involves raising the finance and arranging the venue; deciding on a programme and, in particular, who should be approached to give invited presentations; administering attendance and then publishing the proceedings with due attention to quality control. In any one discipline such as materials science, scores of public-spirited professionals give up their time to organising such conferences every year.

When I embarked on scientific life, long ago, scientific conferences were normally devoted to a carefully circumscribed field of research and participants were numbered in hundreds, or fewer. Today, in materials science, it is common practice to arrange dozens of simultaneous, or parallel, sessions on a great variety of topics, with several thousand participants milling around like ants or bees, often convening in swarms in front of posters carrying scientific information – so many people are desperate to pass on their scientific discoveries that they cannot all be accommodated in the lecture theatres. If such mega-conferences are very conscientiously organised, they can work well. This format of conference is an invention of the (American) Materials Research Society, my favorite society in my profession. Nonetheless, I still have a weakness for the small, focused symposia which were the norm once upon a time, such as the American Gordon Research Conferences which I have mentioned in an earlier chapter.

International co-operation in pursuit of conferences, research projects and publication is primarily the business of International Unions, which are themselves drawn together by an international umbrella body. Among the many dozens of such unions, there are the International Union of Crystallography, and those of Pure and Applied Physics and of Pure and Applied Chemistry; these are not far from the concerns of materials scientists. Unfortunately, there is not as yet an International Union of Materials Science, although some preliminary initiatives have recently been taken to try and create one.

There was a further source of scientifically stimulated foreign travel for me. From the late 1980s onwards, I was elected a member of a number of scientific academies round the world: the Royal Society in England; the Göttingen Academy of Arts and Sciences in Germany; the Academy of Exact, Physical and Natural Sciences in Spain; the Chinese Academy of Sciences; and the Indian National Science Academy – as well as becoming an honorary member of the Indian Institute of Metals and the Materials Research Society of India, a fellow of two American materials societies and an award holder of a third. From 1975, I also received five variegated scientific medals. Each of these events led to an invitation to attend a formal ceremony and, often, associated conferences. I did quite a lot to keep the world's airlines in business.

National academies are distinct from professional societies: some are broad, covering a wide gamut of sciences, others are more restrictive (e.g. medicine only), still others cover sciences and humanities side by side. They are founded in the hope of fostering high standards in research and scholarship, publicly recognizing some of the most deserving of practitioners who have achieved such standards in their work, and advising governments when they are faced with scientific conundrums (such as the pros and cons of genetically modified crops). Academies also elect a smaller proportion of foreigners, sometimes in recognition of candidates' close collaboration with scientists in the country in question.

In the communist and former communist states, academies

also accept the heavy responsibility of running state laboratories (what in America are called the National Laboratories); in the West, academies have declined such responsibilities, which would compromise the academies' important professional independence from government. This distinction is strikingly symbolised by one feature: Fellows of the Royal Society of London ('for promoting excellence in science') and some other western academies are required to pay an annual subscription. If they fail to do so, they are liable to be expelled. The communist and ex-communist academies pay their members a salary and sometimes offer them supplementary benefits, like residences.

Most academies also have scientific journals for the publication of research, originally just by members, but nowadays with a much wider remit. Academies are also among the bodies that organise conferences: the 'discussion meetings' organised by fellows of the Royal Society and their colleagues are today almost unique in publishing verbatim the technical discussions which follow the presentation of lectures, as well as the lectures themselves.

Scientific connections between professors and former research students can also lead to rewarding collaborations which are not exclusively scientific. Thus, in 1979, during a sabbatical year spent in Cambridge during which I sought to recover from the physical and mental stresses of my five years of deanship at Sussex University, Pat and I flew to India for yet another mountain adventure. We joined two of my former Indian research students, Arunachalam (Arun) and Manu Bhatia, and their wives, for a trek in the far northwest of India. We had a little help from the Indian Avalanche Research Establishment, made possible because Arun was by then one of the most senior scientists working for the Indian Defence Ministry and that establishment laboured to keep open high-altitude strategic roads in the Himalaya. Their help came into its own when searchers were needed to look for Manu Bhatia and his wife after they had become impatient one day and went off on their own into a bear-infested wilderness, becoming convincingly lost for a time. At the time, India was governed by a holier-than-thou prime minister who imposed alcoholic prohibition on the entire civil and military service. The army officers at the avalanche establishment, and I, serenely ignored the prohibition and I made myself popular by offering some Scotch malt whisky. I was eventually elected to foreign fellowship of the Indian National Science Academy in spite of my flouting that temporary law!

After these preliminaries, we all six crossed the Rohtang pass in a Land Rover, made rendezvous with an old pony-drover and a small group of ponies and a young guide with a stash of camping equipment, and started on a long trek along an ever-rising track. Initially we stopped off in Kyelong, a village in the Lahaul mountains, and there visited the local headman, an ethnic Tibetan, to whose mistress we were introduced in all her barbaric finery of turquoise, coral and silver. We continued along a steadily rising track, often purely notional although it was supposed to be a strategic motor road in terrain menaced by the unfriendly Chinese. At one point we camped in a meadow, at around 14,000 feet, which years earlier, before the Chinese invaded and sealed off Tibet, had been a trading centre for Indian and Tibetan merchants. Eventually we reached the Bara Lacha La (pass) at 16,000 feet, where Arun conversed affably in their tent with a shivering platoon of Indian soldiers guarding the virtually non-existent road.* I was all for ascending a nearby peak of around 19,000 feet when suddenly Pat complained of the symptoms of altitude sickness which meant that we had at once to descend a thousand feet or so. Later, she confessed that in fact she had had no such trouble, but she did know the nature of the symptoms and so she was able to put up a convincing simulacrum. She had grave doubts about the reliability of the young guide who was proposing to lead the men up that peak, and she thought that if I attempted that ascent, she would probably never see me again, so she had recourse to

_____

*I understand it has been upgraded into a fine motor road today.

the only ploy she knew would keep me off the heights. The other medical non-event that I recall was when, with a whoop, I discovered some thyme growing among rocks and picked it to lend some flavour to our freeze-dried Indian Army rations; however, Arun and Manu were convinced that this unknown herb would poison us all and refused to sanction its use.

The last category of my very numerous foreign trips is that devoted to prolonged journeys in pursuit of specific scientific objectives. Some of these have been the most memorable of all. The first of them was the family's first voyage to the Johns Hopkins University in the United States of America, in 1954, travelling by sea.* There, I wrote the first of my major review articles – on twinned crystals. While preparing that article, I wanted to undertake a small experiment, and for that I needed some advice on how to electropolish the surface of the metal zinc. This kind of polishing does less damage to the surface of a metal than is caused by mechanical polishing with a fine abrasive. A letter to a Frenchman who was the recognized expert in that technique evoked the response that he had no idea how to do it, but added that he had by chance just met an Argentine metallurgist who worked in a factory making zinc-coated batteries, and he knew how. So I wrote next to that Argentine, Jorge Sabato, in Buenos Aires; since I did not know whether he understood English, I wrote in Spanish. The response came by return of post, and consisted of two parts – a long section correcting mistakes in my Spanish, and a shorter one, telling me how to electropolish zinc.

Next year, back in Birmingham, I received a letter from an Argentine agency in London, inviting me, on Sabato's behalf, to go to Buenos Aires for a few weeks and present a course of lectures on modern physical metallurgy. He had in the meantime become chief metallurgist of the Argentine Atomic Energy Commission and, being woefully short of people who knew anything about metallurgy, he resolved to invite a

---

*See Chapter 8.

succession of foreigners to remedy that deficiency. Since he was aware that I knew Spanish, he began with me. The invitation suited me well, since I wanted to buy a car and needed to earn money for that, having spent all of our spare cash during the American year. So, in the summer vacation of 1955, I flew out to Argentina. After my early experiences in Germany and brief exposure to the world of General Franco, I thought I knew what a dictatorship would feel like, but even so, Juan Peron's peculiar, highly arbitrary brand of tyranny – abetted by his populist wife, Eva – came as a surprise. I gave my lectures in Spanish and built up a friendship with Sabato that lasted for decades. During my last few days a popular revolt against Peron's excesses broke out: bloody fighting erupted between his praetorian guard and other parts of the armed forces, and the Navy (which was against Peron) anchored in the River Plate and threatened to bombard Buenos Aires. Pat, at home, listened to the radio news with closer attention than ever before – or since. In short order, Peron and his cronies fled to Madrid, where he was welcomed by General Franco. They did so by hijacking the entire aircraft fleet of Argentine Airlines, and my return ticket was by that airline. I telephoned the British Consul and asked for his help, in view of the extreme emergency. There was a puzzled silence at the other end of the line, followed by, 'And what emergency would that be, sir?' Such sangfroid was too much for me, so I put down the telephone and threw myself on the mercy of another airline, which took my ticket, assured me that they would sort things out by and by, and flew me home to London. I have felt grateful ever since to the Scandinavian Airlines System. I had my cheque and, the following week, I bought my car at auction.

In 1959, I returned to Argentina for a few weeks at Easter, to deliver a course in crystallography at a remote provincial university in northern Patagonia, at a place called San Carlos de Bariloche. Pat was just recovering from a bad bout of pneumonia and the doctor had urged a period of convalescence; I told the Argentine authorities who had invited me that I would come if they paid for Pat's airfare too, and this they agreed to do. We managed to get all our children looked after, the boys at a children's camp. (When we returned after some five weeks, they were inclined to be more satisfied with the parents providence had allocated to them!) On our way home, we stopped for a few days in Brazil, mainly for a much-needed seaside holiday at Copacabana in Rio. First I lectured to a metallurgical society in São Paolo, and then I was more or less kidnapped by the director of a nearby aeronautical college to give yet another talk. He promised to fly Pat and me from his college airstrip to Rio by private plane if I would give that talk. The small aircraft duly materialised and we took off for the old municipal airport in the centre of Rio. On the way we heard the pilot tell air traffic control to keep the big jets at bay for a quarter of an hour while he showed us the delights of Rio: he flew round the Sugar Loaf, 'dive-bombed' Copacabana beach, and flew straight at the huge statue of Christ on the Corcovado hill – which seemed to float on a cloudbase level with the hilltop – before veering off at the last moment. Then he turned courteously to Pat, asked, 'May I land now, madam?' and kissed her hand as he saw her down the aircraft steps. The rest of the Copacabana stay was a slight anticlimax, although Pat was greatly taken by the unlimited supplies of mamão fruit offered by the hotel, and I learnt to appreciate the remarkable looks of the Brazilian beach beauties.

In 1962, I again revisited Argentina, to attend an international metallurgical conference in Patagonia. Two days before it was due to begin, there was another revolution in Buenos Aires. By this time, I knew enough of Argentine political habits to feel confident that this one was not a serious revolt, so I flew in anyway. Once there, I learnt that two eminent Russian metallurgists had failed to appear. So I exploited a once-in-a-lifetime opportunity to send a telegram to Moscow saying, tersely: 'Revolution over now, safe to come.' Next day, they also flew in, slightly shame-faced, bearing gifts for my children.

My Argentine friend, Jorge Sabato, was a truly remarkable

man – rather like my late brother-in-law, Pierre Young. Sabato was not a highly committed researcher with his own hands, but he was a diplomatic genius in organising the institutions which enabled his fellow-countrymen to acquire the skills they needed to become distinguished researchers in their own right. He also had a very good understanding of social organization and of democratic politics. He would have become minister of science after the elections in 1983, which were ushered in by overthrow of the latest set of Argentine tyrants by the British forces which evicted them from the Falkland Islands. Sadly, he developed a lethal cancer shortly before these elections and died just after the first democratic government in many years took up the reins of power. Perhaps the recent economic disasters in that unhappy country would have been less extreme if Sabato had been a member of the government.

In 1960, and 1961, I undertook two working visits to the USA, each time in the summer vacations. The first was to a government research laboratory in Philadelphia, the second to teach a summer course at Stanford University, in California; Pat joined me there once I was settled in. One of my students on that course was Craig Barrett, until recently the chief executive of Intel, the maker of integrated circuits, and the most influential materials scientist in industrial life.*

Pat and I, and David Stevenson, a professor at Stanford, and his wife, went off rock-climbing together in the Sierra Nevada, camping in the back country, and I made the acquaintance of the Sierra Club, a group of climbing and conservation enthusiasts. This was our second visit to the glories of Yosemite, the first having been in 1954; fortunately, it was not the last.

In 1976, I was offered a six-month Commonwealth Visiting Professorship to Monash University, in a suburb of Melbourne, Australia. I was granted a six-month leave from

---

*This is entirely as it should be, since integrated circuits are the most complex artefacts made by man.

my deanship at Sussex University, and off I flew, accompanied by Pat and our youngest daughter Alison, who was in her gap year before going to Oxford. I had leisure to undertake some scientific work again, and also travelled to many universities in Australia on scientific business. Alison learnt even more than I did, especially when she insisted on functioning as a nightclub flowergirl to earn some money; that did not last long. While Alison was roughing it at Alice Springs, Pat and I flew to one of the Whitsuntide islands off the north-east coast, and from there took a boat to the Barrier Reef, upon which we were able to take a memorable walk at low tide. On the way back to terra firma, we were gradually able to smell the approach of land long before it was visible, the only time we have had this remarkable experience.

The most disconcerting of my longterm foreign adventures came when my academic group at Sussex was destroyed by envious engineer colleagues in 1981, and I was offered the headship of the department of metallurgy at the Université de Paris-Sud, to replace my old friend Lacombe, who was retiring. I thought that this would be a haven of restfulness after the unsought excitement of my last years at Sussex, and accepted, to be greeted first of all by a copy of a bitter letter of protest from my future French colleagues, expressing alarm at the prospect of a non-French department head. This letter they sent to the university president, who shot them down collectively in flames. As things started, so they continued. I was encoiled, Laocoon-like, in the snares and folds of French academic bureaucracy, which had rules and limitations for everything I might want to do and tried to force me to do things for which I had no aptitude. Those who resented my appointment made skilled use of the potential for bureaucratic impediments to try and trip me up. I also learnt some new things which helped me later to understand the horrors of the Brussels Commission: my secretary, a very able bilingual woman, and a public employee like all university people in France, was threatened with a sharp drop in her salary or even dismissal when the bureaucrats discovered that she lacked one particular educational certificate. She felt obliged to apply for a 'dérogation'. This extraordinary concept is an official permission to ignore a particular regulation, applied for in competition with a number of other public employees across the length and breadth of France – in fact, a competitive bid to break the law. Only a few such dérogations are granted each year, so this is a singularly effective way of setting employees against each other. The European Commission in Brussels is a hotbed of dérogations. My cynical friend Pierre, my sister's husband, who had his own experience of betrayal by French engineers with whom he was working on Concorde some years earlier, advised me about some realities of French life of which I had been ignorant earlier: one was that to get anything difficult done in France one had to have a network of cronies dating back to one's school and university days, and that in the nature of things was denied to me. I did, however, have a few good and influential scientific friends who turned what would otherwise have been an entirely intolerable experience into something just about manageable, and Pat struck up a close friendship with the English wife of one of these benevolent supporters, Jacques Friedel.

The episode I remember best was when I asked one of the young researchers in my laboratory to buy some paint and paint-rollers in a local shop so that the laboratory could be freshened up a little by our own staff, for we had no money to get the job done professionally. He came back with his tail between his legs, saying that the shop would not accept the university's purchase order because the university never settled its debts.

We rented a flat in the beautiful sixth arondissement of Paris, and Pat had an enjoyable two years there, interacting with the British and Commonwealth Women's Association and improving her French. We enjoyed the excellent restaurants and art exhibitions. After two years, however, in 1983, I could take no more and resigned my chair; we bought the house

153

in Cambridge which we still inhabit and returned to the relative sanity of England with a great sigh of relief, where I took up my academic pension. My two quixotic years in Paris certainly constitute one of the more extreme dislocations in my life.

For a year I was at a loose end scientifically in Cambridge, but at the age of sixty I felt I still had some science left in me. So I negotiated, through American friends from my Sussex days, two six-month attachments, end to end, in 1985–6, first at the central research laboratories of the General Electric Company, in Schenectady, New York State, followed by a spell at the California Institute of Technology in Pasadena, at the opposite extreme of the country. Again, Pat and I had the pleasure of a long transcontinental drive, via a visit to Los Alamos. This year reinjected me into the international scientific circuit, after two years in France which had been almost exclusively devoted to rebarbative administration, and I got a good deal of research done with my own hands, and published in widely read journals. After our return to Cambridge, I was immediately invited to become an honorary research associate in my old department in the university, with an office in the centre of town. I have been happily ensconced there for the past nineteen years.

Cambridge is now the stable centre of my continuing professional life. I avoid all academic politics like the plague it is and occupy myself with scientific – and literary – reading, writing and particularly editing. For a while I also carried out and supervised research, but that is now largely in the past. Pat became involved, from 1983 onwards, with the newly established University of the Third Age in Cambridge, a society of intelligent retired people who both give and receive teaching on a great variety of academic subjects. She has taught variegated topics in English literature for some twenty years now and has become an established figure on the Cambridge intellectual scene.

I still travelled quite frequently, until recently, most often for scientific reasons. Perhaps my eventual epitaph should be the words Homer used of the wanderer Odysseus: *pollá plankte*, that is to say, 'much erring', or to paraphrase, 'driven by fate to wander far and wide'.

14

Politics and Religion

Before the War, I had no understanding of politics and I scarcely ever looked at a newspaper or listened to the radio. The beginnings of political understanding did not touch me until I reached Cambridge. In my first year there, I recall being suddenly struck by the thought that there must be such a thing as 'scientific politics', politics the rightness of which can be scientifically verified, and someone must have tried to persuade me that communism was that thing. It took me only a week or two's reflection to recognize that this notion was total nonsense, and I never returned to it. I came to realize the elementary truth that politics has two entirely distinct aspects: the issue of how a particular settled objective is to be achieved – an issue of means – and the issue of the relative importance of mutually conflicting objectives – an issue of values. No arguments based on facts can ultimately resolve the second kind of issue; to defuse this kind of deep-seated disagreement is the central problem of democratic politics. My values changed by degrees over the past half-century; there is nothing unusual in that.

To the extent that I had political opinions during and just after the War, they were left-wing, if only mildly so. When I first came to know Pat's family, in 1945, I would daringly engage them – which meant primarily her father – in political dispute. He was a deeply convinced conservative, and it did not take me long to recognize that his politics were based on extensive experience, a fact which gave me pause in formulating my own opinions. He was a man who had worked his way up from extremely humble beginnings, and that coloured all his values.

I did not discuss politics with poppa. Perhaps it would be more accurate to say that he did not discuss politics with me. I do know that he felt extremely indignant about having been interned, and while he was in internment in England he put considerable selfless efforts into dissuading the camp authorities from putting the fathers of families into the ships on which some internees were sent to Australia and Canada in order to lighten the burden on the British camps; poppa recognized that those ships were at considerable risk of being sunk, and some indeed were. Before the War, on a continental holiday, he showed me trenches left over from the First World War and spoke eloquently about what had happened there. That was poppa's kind of politics. As for normal national politics, I never knew how poppa voted in the general elections of 1950 and after, or whether he voted at all.

While I was working at the Harwell Laboratory, a general election was called in 1950. In the campaign for this, at the age of twenty-five I was still sufficiently leftwing in outlook to agree to undertake some door-to-door canvassing for the Labour Party. I have a sharp memory of knocking at one modest door in Harwell village, with a view to obtaining a tick on a canvassing form, and asking the old man who appeared whether he was willing to indicate to me how he planned to vote. He gazed at me mildly and remarked, 'They do say as how the poll is secret'. I had no response to this, and stopped canvassing. At this same time I had occasion to put the beat-up old car I had acquired, with a small legacy from my grandfather, into the garage for urgent attention, and place a facetious handwritten notice in the rear window: 'Join the floating voters!' When I collected the car, someone had scribbled underneath: 'Floating voters sink!' Labour won that election – just – with a very sharply reduced majority. The following year it lost its majority altogether. Some floating voters had sunk the Party.

During the four years I was working at Harwell, 1947–51, I became fully aware of world events for the first time. At the rooming-house in Abingdon, where Pat and I lived during 1948–49, I became very emotionally involved with the Berlin Airlift, which began in July 1948 in response to the Soviet Union's barring of all road and rail traffic between Berlin and the West. Several of us young scientists in the common room in that rooming-house would discuss these events intensely, with expressions of great indignation. One figure among us sat hunched in his armchair, hidden behind the broad pages of *The Times*. That figure was the bachelor recluse, Klaus Fuchs, head of theoretical physics at Harwell, who two years later was to be unmasked as a wartime atomic spy for the Russians. I have often wondered how in his heart he reacted to what he heard us say about the Russians. Another, earlier event which had a lasting effect on my thinking was the prolonged miners' strike in the very severe winter of 1946–47, soon after the mines had been nationalised by the Labour Government in the hope of preventing the kind of desperate strikes which had taken place in Britain in 1926. Ever after the events of that postwar winter, when workplaces had to be closed and homes were often unheated, I was anxiously waiting for the kind of trade union reform that Mrs Thatcher was to put into effect thirty-five years later. Labour tried half-heartedly to bring about such reforms but was unable to effect them. In essence, the Berlin Airlift cured me of the slightest desire to embrace the left wing, and the miners' strike, so early in my adult life, set me off on my steady drift towards conservative views. If these had not sufficed, the huge impact of the Hungarian uprising against the Russians of 1956 and the hordes of young people who escaped from Hungary and came as refugees to Britain, some as guests in my home, would have done the job.

I cannot remember how I voted in 1951, but at subsequent elections for a while I supported the Conservatives. I am sure I voted for Macmillan's Conservative party in 1959, when still only in my mid-thirties. This suggests to me that my

159

political drift was not just, as some of my children are apt to believe with regret, the frequently observed old men's tendency to become reactionary dinosaurs. I was too young for that.

My lack of dinosaur status can perhaps be deduced from something that happened in 1953. My friend Frank Nabarro, a distinguished but somewhat impoverished British physicist in his mid-thirties, with whom I had visited Germany the year before, had been offered and accepted a chair of physics at the University of the Witwatersrand, in Johannesburg, and had just taken up the post. A letter from him reached me soon afterwards, inviting me to join him as a second professor (of metal physics). I was only twenty-eight and briefly tempted – after all, I was impoverished too. As it happened, the anti-apartheid priest, Father Huddleston, who was touring Britain in pursuit of his convictions, was due to speak in Birmingham and I attended his meeting. I sent up an anonymous question: 'What advice would you give to a young British professional man thinking of taking up a post in South Africa?' His answer was clear: if you are single, go and take the risk of opposing the cruelties of the system, but if you are married and have, or plan to have children, don't even think of going. Your children are likely to be corrupted, and you may be imprisoned and leave them destitute. In complete agreement with Pat, I turned the offer down. Frank Nabarro, who had been strongly leftwing in his politics a few months before, when he was still in Britain, claimed at the time not to understand my decision at all.

Macmillan's administration was something of a disappointment (I was still too young to recognize that this is eventually true of *all* administrations) and when, in the infamous Night of the Long Knives in July 1962, Macmillan dismissed seven cabinet ministers, I began to look to the Liberals. In March of that same year, in a by-election in Orpington, Kent, a young engineer, thirty-three-year-old Eric Lubbock, had been elected Liberal member of parliament by an astounding majority of 7,855 votes, overturning a Conservative majority of 14,760 from three years earlier. This extraordinary by-election was enormously influential and its meaning endlessly analysed at the time. For the next eleven years I was a Liberal supporter and in North Wales, in 1964, I was quite active in their support at a parliamentary general election.

Eric Lubbock remained an MP for only eight years before the pendulum swung again, but thereafter he was able to reclaim the inherited peerage that he had shrugged off earlier and became the Liberal peer, Lord Avebury. In 1999, when Blair's government expelled most of the hereditary lords from the House of Lords, without any idea what to put in their place, Lord Avebury was one of the small number elected by his peers to stay in the House. He has remained actively involved with human rights throughout his years in Parliament and is widely admired.

Some time after I moved to Sussex University, probably in 1966, I was invited to help the Liberal Party as a scientific adviser, and was actively involved in this way until 1973. I have kept a number of letters which show that I took this task very seriously. For instance, the Liberal peer Lord Byers solicited my help in assembling arguments relating to the Swann Report of 1969, devoted to the flow into employment of scientists and engineers, a matter of considerable political concern at that time: I sent Lord Byers a long analysis of arguments to help him as Liberal spokesman in the House of Lords. Some years later, I gave similar help to Lord Avebury over a government 'green paper' on the Civil Service, and visited him repeatedly in Parliament. This period is the closest I have ever come to active involvement in democratic politics.

At one point during this involvement of mine with the Liberals, Pat decided to stand in Sussex as a local councillor in the Liberal interest. The area where we then lived was intensely Conservative, and for many years nobody had stood in opposition to successive Conservative candidates, who had thus always enjoyed a walkover. Although Pat obtained only about 25% of the vote, that was much more than anyone had expected, and many voters came up to her and told her that, while they held Conservative opinions, they approved of her stand and had voted for her! We were both much heartened by this illustration of independent thinking by the voters. When, however, in my retirement, I was urged to stand for election to the local City Council, my children eloquently dissuaded me.

By 1973, after a short period of Conservative rule, Labour had again gained power, and we were now in a six-year period when the economy steadily, and rapidly, went downhill, the trade unions became immensely powerful and inflation reached (by British standards) dizzy heights. From this time on my central objective was to see a curb to socialist power, and I judged that the Conservatives were more likely to bring that about than the Liberals. From that time on, for the past thirty years, I have been a steadfast supporter of the Conservatives. When Margaret Thatcher won her famous victory in 1979, I was immensely relieved and never shifted from that reaction, in spite of the fact that the vast majority of British academics – like those in America – were and are liberals, socialists or Democrats (in the American sense) and my support for Mrs Thatcher was regarded by many of my friends – and more of my foes – as quite against nature.

At this point, I want to return briefly to the students' revolt of 1968–70. I found that reactions to this were strongly correlated with people's general political stance. As I write this, in mid-2003, a magazine to which I subscribe quotes Jack Lang, an exceptionally nationalistic and culturally anti-American French socialist, who has drifted in and out of ministerial portfolios in France like a yo-yo. He wrote:

May 1968 was a grand movement of liberation in the American sense, but also a movement of simple respiration. The French state then [under President Charles de Gaulle] was a symbol of oppression. It seemed to have a lid on everything, with state-run television and radio putting out permanent propaganda. Suddenly, it appeared that the state wasn't all-powerful after all, and for many of us things seemed to even smell different. What we didn't sense was the real worry the revolt provoked in traditional France...

That worry was enough for de Gaulle to disappear for some days to the embrace of his army. As an Englishman I have no cause to sympathise with de Gaulle, who, although he did great things for his country, was in his own very different way as obnoxious as Jack Lang, but Lang's reminiscence does show how reactions to the revolt differed between those who were not ashamed to be labelled as bourgeois and the Left with its revolutionary instincts that go all the way back to 1789. Sussex University, like a number of other universities around 'the West', was a hotbed of leftwing extremists among the faculty and many of them venerated the rebellious students who destroyed the spirit and urbanity of the university, and supported them in their efforts. I was also staggered by the long-term romantic attachment to the memory of the barricades of those who had briefly lounged behind them. In 1985, while I was in the USA, I invited for dinner an American scientist who had been a student at Columbia University in the late 1960s, and began to tell him how the events at Sussex had seemed to me. He became very angry and praised the spirit of the revolutionaries without reserve – nearly twenty years after the event.

Something else, looking back, contributed to the intensity of my reaction to the student revolt. I had been a student during the War, and the sense of almost unbelievable privilege which that engendered in me was unforgettable. During the War, we, the students, would never have considered for a moment complaining about our food or our room rents or the quality of our teaching or the locking of college gates at midnight: we were too astonished that we were there at all. The sense of rampant ingratitude in the privileged students of the late 1960s was very hard to come to terms with, for someone with my kind of experience.

Looking back, I recognize that I was by temperament

altogether immune to the deification of causeless anger, which is one way of perceiving the student revolt. I had discovered this about myself some years earlier, in 1956, when the first of the 'angry young men', the dramatist John Osborne, wrote *Look Back in Anger*. Pat and I saw the play in Birmingham that same year and were profoundly repelled by it; that reaction would have been greeted by Osborne, had he known of it, as a mark of his success. The central figure is a young graduate who has opted out, runs a sweet stall in a town market, tyrannises his patient wife and seeks to terrorise her into rejecting her bourgeois parents. He has nothing to rebel against, but he rebels anyway. The avant-garde welcomed Osborne with open arms. Twenty years later, when we were all three in Australia in 1976, we took our nineteen-year-old daughter Alison to see a revival of that play, and she was entranced by it. There have not been many occasions when we reacted with total mystification to our children's preferences, but this was one of them. It turned out that the play had been a set text when she was in the final stages of her school career. As I write this, in 2003, I have just read an extract from a famous theatre director's diary, in which John Osborne appears as a monster of self-pity, when his brief period of adulation by the fickle glitterati of the London social scene had passed. Self-pity is indeed one of the most damaging and unpleasant emotions, and I am glad to have been inoculated against it by one of my schoolteachers.

That leaves Europe. By now, readers will not be surprised to learn that I progressively turned against the pretensions of the colossus of Brussels. In the very early days of what was to become the European Economic Community and then the European Union, I was distinctly sympathetic. The European Coal and Steel Community, the very first organisation to be established on that long path, held its first meeting in January 1953. Later that year it fell to me, as a lecturer at Birmingham University, to lead a students' tour of metallurgical laboratories in France, Germany and Luxembourg, and I conceived the idea of conducting the students round the brand new Coal and Steel building in Luxembourg. To my surprise, they were extremely resistant to this particular element of the tour – perhaps they sensed that they were being subjected to a form of propaganda. In 1974, when, after de Gaulle's monstrously ungrateful, though probably justified, reaction to the first British application to join the emerging Community, my country had a second bite at the cherry and a referendum was called on the issue, I was still ready to vote in favour of what was very firmly (and very deceitfully) presented to the British voter as an exclusively economic enterprise. Thereafter, I began to cool. My two years in France, exposed to French attitudes to 'les anglo-saxons' accelerated my slide, and by the time Pat and I returned to Cambridge in 1983 my hostility had become engrained. Our son Andrew undertook more than one difficult task in Brussels, on secondment from the home civil service – even earning a decoration from the British government for one of these achievements, an honour which he received at the hands of the Queen, while our eldest son, Martin, who is a consultant ecologist, gets a good deal of his funding from Brussels. Unfortunately, neither of these facts could reconcile me to the trends of the European enterprise, and to the ceaseless avalanche of directives (odious word!) falling on my country from Brussels. For some years in the early 1990s I acted as coordinator for a group of Italian, Spanish and French researchers, applying for European research money. The administrative procedures were so unbelievably rigid and time-consuming that after a while I bowed out, even though the people in Brussels seemed to be keen on financing us.

The European imbroglio perfectly illustrates my point about the conflict between mutually incompatible values. The notion that peace can be enforced in Europe only by central rule (or, to use the favourite alternative term, by the pooling of sovereignty) has something – not very much – going for it. Peace derives, I believe, from the ubiquity of sound democratic forms of government, the very feature which is most lacking in Brussels. The preservation of the supremacy of our long-established and now-endangered British Parliament and of long-cherished British liberties is a counter-value. Each of us in Britain, if we think about these matters at all, has to decide which consideration should have primacy. Economic arguments are altogether secondary in the face of these two central values. I have read numerous articles, pamphlets and books about the European enterprise, of all political colours, and my mind is now made up: my financial contributions go to support that counter-value.

It is a source of regret to many in England that successive governments of the United States have felt it necessary to urge England to become ever more closely involved with the colossus of Brussels. American presidents, it seems, want a single telephone number to call when a world crisis arises. It is more important, I think, to have a list of several telephone numbers, one of which belongs to a true friend.

I have painted a political self-portrait, with quite sufficient chiaroscuro for this concise account. I now turn to religion.

All my grandparents were unmistakably Jewish and my parents, therefore, likewise. My paternal grandfather was an observant Jew, my maternal one, so far as I was able to determine, was not. At the age of six I was sent to a Jewish school in Fürth just to learn the elements of Hebrew, but that had hardly begun when I was sent away to boarding school, where no Jewish background was available. Then the world was turned upside down in 1933 and I was not exposed to any religious influences, Jewish or otherwise, until the headmaster of Maiden Erlegh school in 1936 forced me to attend Anglican Sunday services. These, however, rolled off my back without leaving any drops behind. My father in London never took me to synagogue, though he himself observed the high holidays. There was never any talk of bar mitzvah and we attended only one passover supper. Things changed a little in 1941, when I was home from my Cumbrian school for the holidays. I was sixteen and, to give me some company of my own age, poppa pushed me to attend a Jewish youth club not far from his home in north-west London. There

I made a second attempt to learn some Hebrew, but I found the incentive too weak to persist. What was memorable at that club, however, was the political indoctrination. There was a fiery young man who sought to persuade us all that there was no future for us Jews in Britain, that the German experience had shown that assimilation was a hopeless pipedream. Our duty was, in the ungrammatical phrase taken (I think) from the Yiddish, to 'make aliyah', to prepare ourselves to emigrate to the coming Jewish national home, join a kibbutz and work as farmers. Seven years were yet to elapse before Israel was declared a state. The propaganda was so fierce and unremitting – especially when I attended a Jewish farming interlude to help with a wartime harvest somewhere in England – that I reacted with growing hostility. I simply did not believe the assertion that the British would turn against me as a Jew and I dropped the youth club. That was my last attempt to become a 'good Jew'. In the sixty-nine years I have lived in Britain, only two people have shown me any slight signs of antisemitism; I reckon that my response in 1941 has been justified by experience. I have never thought of myself as belonging to a chosen people, not even in my capacity as an Englishman! I believe that concept to be deplorable – unless 'chosen' refers to my own rôle in creating an identity for myself. Still less, as one of the kohanim, do I want to be an elect among the chosen. I still read and reflect on a variety of books about the religious experience generally, and venerate the miraculous English of the Authorised Version of the Bible. At one point, I experimented with attendance at a group of humanists, but soon desisted when I found that some of them were militant atheists. I am also well aware of the rôle of religious conviction in providing an externally sanctioned system of morality. But utilitarian considerations like this simply do not suffice to make me a religious person, and I cannot perceive faith in itself as a form of virtue, so I put up with being what Pat calls me – a 'virtuous heathen'. or approximately so. Having 'married out' of my native faith does not worry me in the slightest, and it never has done.

167

I am afraid that my apostasy from orthodox Judaism would have appalled my paternal grandfather, Emil, who was a deeply observant Jew. His own father had been leader of a major Jewish community in a small German town and clearly was descended from a line of 'good Jews'. Emil, as I have recently discovered, excoriated one of his daughters when she married 'out' of the religion and refused to have any further contact with her – the common, deplorable response of devout Jews to their children's out-marriages. The reaction of my eldest son to this discovery was very forceful: my children, like me, are averse to ritual observances.

I have long harboured sympathy for Tibetan Buddhism and the Tibetan people; that probably goes back to my reading of a book about the early Everest expeditions in the 1920s, and then a remarkable book by the mountaineer and scholar Marco Pallis, *Peaks and Lamas*. I do not mean that I paid attention to the collection of demons and benevolent spirits depicted on Buddhism's painted t'hankas; what impressed me, and impresses me still, is the extraordinary sweetness of nature of many Tibetans, and their characteristic tolerance. Pallis writes at some length of the Buddhist concept of a 'translator', a scholar who studies other religions in great depth before communicating their essence to his fellow-Buddhists, without thereby seeking to constrain their own choice of beliefs. Buddhists worship no god – the Buddha himself is not regarded as one; their figures of veneration are multiple. Tolerance is sufficiently rare in the monotheistic faiths for Tibetan attitudes to make an impression on a natural sceptic like myself. In the 1960s and 1970s I financially supported a young Tibetan refugee boy, Samdup Phuntsok, in India and built up a personal relationship with him which lasts to this day. I also repeatedly visited groups of Tibetan refugees in northern India.

Pat was an Anglican by birth. After we were married, she began a long experiment with the Society of Friends – the Quakers – whom she found congenial and spiritually restorative, though she could not quite go along with their unconditional pacifism. I sometimes went with her, and during a summer working in Philadelphia in 1960 I had several weeks of close involvement with the long-established Quakers there, but it did not 'take'.

I conclude by returning to a consideration which is both political and religious: my attitude to present-day Germany. As I indicated earlier in this Memoir, my first return to Germany in 1952 was distinctly traumatic, and for some years after that I kept away. The generous friendship of Peter Haasen and his wife, however, and progressively closer relationships with other German scientists such as Hans Warlimont and Erhard Hornbogen, overcame my scruples and nowadays I am able to travel to conferences in Germany without any problem. The one thing I have never been able to bring myself to do was to take a holiday in Germany.

I have soaked myself in the extensive literature about the long history of the Jews in Germany, about the Weimar Republic and why it collapsed so disastrously, and how the Germans themselves reacted to the gradually irresistible awareness of what they had allowed to happen in their beautiful land. A recent book by the eminent American historian Peter Gay (formerly Fröhlich), entitled *My German Problem*, was particularly illuminating. His personal traumas, before he was able to escape in 1938, gave him more reason than I ever had to find Germany intolerable, but he worked through that initial response, by degrees. There is even one strange book by an unknown German diplomat, Jörg von Uthmann, that compares the politics of Germans, Jews and communists and claims to find remarkable points of parallelism. The story of the desperate links between the Germans and the Jews will provide raw material for historians for decades to come. My responsibility is to find tolerance in my heart and my experience, in my later years, of genuine friendship in my native country has enabled me to do that. The primary dislocation of my youth has been set right.

15

Posterity

My posterity consists of those to whom I have passed on my genes, and others to whom I have sought to pass on my scientific expertise. My wife and I are intensely proud of our children and their many achievements, and deeply touched by their determination to keep in close and frequent touch with us. However, their personalities and careers do not belong in this Memoir, so I will merely repeat that we have four children and twelve grandchildren.

My scientific posterity includes some twenty former graduate students who took their doctorates with my advice, and some twenty-five postdoctoral research fellows who worked with me over the years at Birmingham, Bangor, Sussex and Paris universities and, more recently, in American institutions and in Cambridge. I remain in some degree of contact with most of these; the majority of them live abroad, in all parts of the world. I particularly value my many friends in India and China. In a broader sense, the nearly 200 students who obtained bachelor's degrees in materials science at Sussex also form part of my scientific posterity. I still receive requests every year to write letters in support of promotions, tenure, prizes and awards for former students, and for other people with whom I have worked or who have written articles or books for me. Many of these old colleagues come and visit me when they are in my country, and over the years I have persuaded a number of them to write contributions to books or encyclopedias that I have edited. The sense of community with them is very strong.

In 1999, my wife and I attended a scientific NATO conference held in Greece. During the usual afternoon of repose, we walked on a beach and an Algerian student who was one of the participants came up to me and asked for 'a word of wisdom'. What elderly scientist can withstand such a request? So I told him that there is no such thing as Algerian science or Greek science or British science but only the international community of scientists which he should cultivate as much as he could. He had a good chance of flourishing scientifically, I assured him, if he kept his gaze fixed on the wide world. What I told the young man was perhaps a slight exaggeration, but in essence it represented what I truly believe.

My feelings about the international community of science which my scientific posterity inhabits can best be conveyed by quoting some remarks my wife made in a touching after-dinner speech she delivered on the occasion of my 75th birthday, which chanced to coincide with that 1999 scientific meeting. Her remarks met such a positive response that they were published in the proceedings of the meeting – the only after-dinner speech which I have ever seen immortalised in this way.

A major invariance in his life has been his idealism about science. There were students in our time – no doubt there always are – who thought that a cynical attitude to life and work was evidence of maturity. Robert had no need to fake maturity. A disrupted childhood had thrust independence and maturity upon him. He was too aware of the value of life to be cynical. And he had gained three languages; and an intimate understanding of three nations; and a permanent interest in the way peoples both resemble and differ from each other. *Perhaps science appealed to him as a neutral area where the great divisions of humanity are put aside in the pursuit of knowledge, a pursuit with many achievements, but never complete...* [My italics.]

As Robert's work expanded and I became busy with children, I could no longer follow the details of his work.

He went to conferences, he had research students, and imperceptibly the network started to grow. A fine miscellaneous lot they were that he would bring home for a drink, for dinner, or a bed for the night: important and unimportant, local and foreign, he never explained them, and of course I enjoyed them when they were not inconvenient. Once I remember suggesting that an invitation he was planning didn't suit me. 'We must have them,' he said. 'This man and his wife are visitors in a strange country. They must be welcomed. They must see how people here live.' Unanswerable.

Besides foreign visitors there were the research students, whom we must entertain, with other colleagues, so that they could start their own networks; and whom he always kept in touch with, exchanging advice and information, over the years, and who recurred at intervals when they were in our country, or we were in theirs.

There were occasions when we ourselves spent periods abroad, and received hospitality, and tried to learn other people's strange ways, and to understand these ways as resulting from climate, and history, and cultural traditions: some of them sensible even if different from our splendid English habits – and where not entirely sensible, yet it would be presumptuous in us to expect to alter them. And sometimes one really can learn something useful. I remember being in the USA in 1954. Rationing had not quite ended in Britain. We had had years of surviving by putting up with things. The Americans seemed to me to have no power of endurance; when something was wrong they wanted to put it right instantly. They are right. We had spent too long accepting things and it was time to demand that they improve. I hope I also learnt to imitate their marvellous hospitality. Robert had no need to learn either. He has always been unthinkingly generous, and impatient when things aren't right...

Well, the research was good, but is now in the past. The supervising of research has gradually ceased. But the network of friendships that has grown from those shared researches, the exchanges of knowledge and advice, *that* continues. The transmission of knowledge in the form of journalism, editing other people's writing and doing his own, *that* continues. **And the thing that is invariant is the belief in the importance of a form of internationalism that really works, a pursuit of truth that unites mankind.**

That last sentence expresses, as closely as a single sentence can, what has kept my enthusiasm for science alive for so many years.

16

The Art of Belonging

You that love England, who have an ear for her music,
The slow movement of clouds in benediction,
Clear arias of light thrilling over her uplands,
Over the chords of summer sustained peacefully.

Those lines by Cecil Day-Lewis incorporate much that speaks to me: music and mountains, light and image, and England herself. England is an entity to which I for many years longed to belong, before that privilege was finally accorded to me.

* * *

I travelled among unknown men,
In lands beyond the sea;
Nor England! did I know till then
What love I bore to thee.

William Wordsworth was born in England at a time when foreign travel was far more demanding than it is now. He had to travel among unknown men to unlock what was in his heart already; I took refuge here from known men, and that put the love of which he writes into my heart too.

* * *

General good is the plea of the scoundrel, hypocrite and
    flatterer:
For Art and Science cannot exist but in minutely organized
    particulars.

William Blake, who was no friend of Science ('May God us
keep / From single vision and Newton's sleep'), nevertheless
perceived something essential that united what he really cared
for, Art, with Science. Perhaps Blake put his finger on what
speaks eloquently to a scientist like me from the world of
Art. I belong to Art as much as to Science – I cannot help it.
I have long loved these lines by Blake.

*   *   *

I fear that perhaps I am being too solemn, but then, to write
about the Art of Belonging without being a little solemn is
impossible. All I can hope to do is to eschew those characteristics
of which Shakespeare, in *The Merchant of Venice*, wrote
sardonically:

> There are a sort of men whose visages
> Do cream and mantle like a standing pond,
> And do a wilful stillness entertain,
> With purpose to be dressed in an opinion
> Of wisdom, gravity, profound conceit;
> As who should say, 'I am Sir Oracle,
> And when I ope my lips let no dog bark'!

*   *   *

Throughout this Memoir, without until now using the phrase,
I have focused on the vital necessity of 'a sense of belonging'
– belonging to my ancestors and parents, though I have not
found that always straightforward; belonging to England after
years as a stateless refugee from Nazidom; belonging to a
solid marriage, with its right and proper concomitant, a bevy

176

of children and grandchildren; belonging to the great world of science and the community of one's fellow-practitioners, junior and senior; and, less obviously, belonging to the community of those who venerate the English language in all its unmatched subtlety and variety, to the community of art-lovers, and to the community of those who frequent the mountain heights. Such a multiple sense of belonging is, I believe, an essential component of mental equilibrium. It also enables one to avoid indolence and provides a strong spring for daily action. Multiple belonging, in this sense, has enabled me to vanquish the earlier dislocations in my life.

I have tried also to achieve a sense of belonging to the world of universities, but that has not been so straightforward, as these institutions have become progressively bureaucratised and politicised. Cambridge, where now I dwell contentedly, has successfully maintained its intellectual edge, though it is for ever being sniped at by the politicians. Its mode of governance is so extremely democratic that decision-making is sometimes almost paralysed. This is a built-in defect of extreme democracy, but there are those who judge that defect a price worth paying to avoid exclusive control by administrators focused on good order. So it would be fair to say that my sense of belonging to Cambridge has solidified, but my corresponding sense of belonging to the wider academic world has attenuated somewhat.

The sense of belonging to England, or alternatively to the more shadowy concept of 'Britain', is in harsh and inescapable conflict with a sense of belonging to Europe. In spite of my endless travel to European lands and my widely spread network of friends there, I simply cannot summon up loyalty to the artificial construct of the European Union, and the threat of a federation which would offer to its constituent regions much less autonomy than is possessed by the States of the USA. As for so many other Britons, my innate sense of community with the United States of America is much closer.

The sense of belonging which matters most to me is to the

177

world of scientific research and communication, and that is of its essence, as my wife has so clearly expressed it, an international pursuit which brings the nations closer together. Science offers a most welcome respite from petty politics: for me, it encapsulates the Art of Belonging.